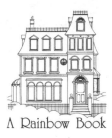

A Rainbow Book

Praise for *Eavesdropping*—

"This is THE book for mature women and those in anyone's life—including my own. The understanding and advice about everything from traveling alone (demand a good table at a restaurant, stay in bed and breakfasts) to dealing with profound loss (sometimes means liberation, don't be a victim) are truly words to live by. Onward!"

—Jim Lehrer, *The News Hour* (PBS)

"A table of insight set before you — as you dine with women who share their collective experience, knowledge and some of life's greatest lessons — to savor for years to come."

—Susie Graham, coauthor of *When One Door Closes: A Teen's Inspiring Journey and Living Legacy*

"I found my tribe. As you integrate the wisdom of these pages from 'The Pages,' you will be introduced to timeless wisdom. A wisdom that is embraced when we realize that we are a member of a precious tribe called ever-evolving women."

—Linda M. Sacha, author of *Queen for a Day*

"*Eavesdropping* uses an innovated delivery style that attracts and holds a reader's interest throughout the book. Although written by and for women, I recommend this book for all men over 50 to 'listen in' on the open, honest, and intimate conversations of mature women a/k/a, 'The Pages.' "

—Richard J. Van Ness, Ph.D., author of *Count Your Beans! — A Pathway to Riches*

continued on the following page

"Uplifting and inspiring . . . provides a grounded perspective and approach toward the many faceted aspects women face as we age."

–Jill S. Creech, P.E.

"The one thing we most want from life is to be happy. Easy to say . . . harder to do. As we tack on the years, the challenges change but the happiness search continues. Well . . . look no more. Here come 'The Pages' ready to let you in on their discoveries. Be ready to get a whole bunch happier."

–Tom Welch, America's Career Coach,
author of *Work Happy Live Healthy*

"An involving, very direct book that includes honest and frank discussions by a number of women over a period of time expressing their concerns and experiences as they age into older members of our society. The book covers very different life styles and attitudes, and is very well handled. You'll enjoy reading it."

–Connie Houser, author of 16 nonfiction titles, including
The Letters, Portrait of an Artist, Jim Houser
and the novel, *Absolute Power!*

"It has been very validating to discover that the very issues my friends and I have been discussing this past year – all of us in our 60's – are those the real women in these pages are grappling with as well: how to stay open to what life may offer after loss or change; returning to what seems significant and interesting to each of us; pursuing those interests with excitement about where they might take us; questioning if there is sex after 65; and retaining a lively sense of humor throughout the journey. The book is a meaningful and inspiring read."

–Nancy Alvarez, author of *Little Nancy: The Journey Home*

EAVESDROPPING

❦❧❦❧❦❧

As Real Women Talk About the Gifts and Challenges of Aging

KENDRA T. BROWN, PH.D.

in collaboration with

"THE PAGES"

Rainbow Books, Inc.
FLORIDA

Eavesdropping: As Real Women Talk About the Gifts and Challenges of Aging
© 2012 by Kendra T. Brown, Ph.D.

Softcover ISBN 978-1-56825-137-0
ePub ISBN 978-1-56825-153-0

Cover design and illustrations by Michael Hardy
(HardyIllustration.com)

Published by
Rainbow Books, Inc.
P. O. Box 430, Highland City, FL 33846-0430

Editorial Offices and Wholesale/Distributor Orders
Telephone: (863) 648-4420 • RBIbooks@aol.com • www.RainbowBooksInc.com

Author's Website
KendraBrownPh.D.com

Individuals' Orders
Toll-free Telephone (800) 431-1579
www.Amazon.com • www.BookCH.com • www.AllBookStores.com

First Edition 2012
16 15 14 13 12   7 6 5 4 3 2 1
Printed in the United States of America.

With special acknowledgment and thanks to Pat Austin, who developed the voice of The Eavesdropper and whose creativity and sense of humor guided the fictional format.

Special thanks to Terry Kinane Gray, who facilitated and guided the business aspects of the book and Lisa Freeman, who provided special creative ideas and text.

And last, but not least, my thanks to my husband, Mac Stuckey, for his ongoing support, especially through this project, and for his wisdom and sage advice.

Contents

EAVESDROPPING

*As Real Women Talk
About the Gifts
and Challenges of Aging*

Prologue

O
ur story began when a young woman came to the library to work on her master's thesis. Her work was interrupted by the voices of older women in the meeting room on the other side of the wall. She was immediately intrigued by them and recorded what she heard while eavesdropping.

These women seemed clear in their purpose for meeting — to discuss issues they considered vital for all women to question and consider. They hoped to write a book that summarized their discussions, and they intended to invigorate and motivate others. The women, who decided to call themselves *The Pages*, quickly displayed differing views; and they were striking in their openness, candor and humor.

Sometime later, she heard one of The Pages recalling that first meeting:

> "The first time we met with great expectations and some trepidation, we were a combination of old friends, professional associates and perfect strangers. In some of our minds there

was the question, 'How, or why, was I chosen?' It was an impressive group, and excitement competed with awe.

"And then we started to talk and talk and talk, and it all became clear. We weren't there because of *what* we had achieved, but rather what we had confronted, endured — and somehow overcome — *to* achieve. Although we had all succeeded in different areas and at different tasks, the roads we had traveled were strikingly familiar.

"So why did we get to this position, when so many women falter, stall, detour and fail? If we could figure that out — could we be helpful to others?"

∼

The collaborating authors of this book, the actual "Pages," met regularly for about three years, dedicated to their goal. Their illustrative stories, their opinions, beliefs and diverse points of view are expressed by fictional counterparts; their names have been changed. While there are no one-on-one correlations between the fictional Pages and the real women, the content of the meetings is true. Their collective work is dedicated to women everywhere of all ages.

How It All Began.

The Pages meet and the Eavesdropper listens

Second floors of libraries have always been places of comfort for me – havens of quiet above the busy first floor, a treasure trove of information all within my reach.

So, of course, when I started working in earnest on my master's thesis, I headed straight for the library's second floor, secured a small study room with perfect natural light and a strong wireless connection, and staked out my territory. With my children in school every morning, I coveted my time to return to a world I love, the world of literature – populated with vibrant characters created through the genius of my favorite writers.

Imagine, then, my annoyance when I realized the wall to my right was also the wall of the library's meeting room, and, apparently, it was paper-thin, because voices – women's voices – were disturbing my sanctuary. I wondered if I should give up the perfect, natural light and move, or if could I convert their voices into white noise and ignore them as meaningless background.

I had nested in "my" space. I tried, at first, to ignore "them", but my intentions were short lived. My curiosity vetoed my resolve, as I listened to their introductions.

There were six of them: Eleanor, Laura, Ellen, Kelly, Rachel and Susan. I marveled at the ease with which they interacted, even though it was obviously their first meeting. There were solemn moments, exclamations of surprise, gentle wisecracks — the whole fabric of the gathering punctuated often by friendly laughter. Despite myself, I started picturing the women who spoke, imagining whole scenarios for their lives, as each of them, in turn, provided basic background information.

For what purpose, I wondered, has such a varied group been pulled together? They were obviously bright and energetic. I was impressed by their accomplishments: several had reached the top rungs of corporate ladders, many of them had been and were still active as leaders in philanthropic organizations. A couple of them had been university professors, while another had helped guide a consulting firm to success. They mentioned their roles as wives, mothers and grandmothers as major aspects of their histories.

Although the group members were from differing backgrounds and varied slightly in age from each other, they were all seemingly past many of the things that occupied my thoughts: establishing a career, raising children and balancing all of that within a married or intimate relationship. However, something about their intensity and sense of purpose kept me tuned in, like a child at a keyhole, listening to private adult conversations.

∽

"So, Eleanor," said a voice I came to recognize as that of Susan, "I'm enjoying this conversation, but just why have you asked us to come together today?"

Eleanor, obviously the organizer of the meeting, responded — in a voice tinged with a sweet Southern accent. "You've been invited to participate in a kind of think tank. Some of you I know personally. Those people, in turn, have invited others. So, I don't know all of you.

But I hope that will change soon. I'm very committed to investigating a number of themes that have emerged in my therapy sessions with women, specifically with older women. I'd like this group to discuss these issues, and, hopefully, our discussions may help other women. We might even write a book based on our meetings."

There were favorable responses almost instantly.

"I'm excited already!" said one.

"Before we book our tickets to the *Today* show," Eleanor said with a hint of amusement, "let me explain more about how this started. In my private practice, I've been amazed to see so many women who are very depressed – despite having adequate resources of money, time, experience and education. It saddens and frustrates me to see how lost they seem."

"That's surprising," someone responded. "With resources and time, what's the problem?"

Eleanor went on, "What I've surmised is this: they've come to a certain age where they've run out of role models. Longevity, it seems, has a 'down side' as well as an 'up side'. They've outlived the roles and responsibilities they knew so well – roles that gave them a sense of self, of purpose and pride of accomplishment. Now, because they're living longer than their role models did, there is time left over, and they don't have a clue how to fill it. They haven't found new purposes, fresh goals, or new activities in which they can succeed. So, many are stuck, still concentrating their attention on their spouses, or on their children, who are now busy adults. As a result, when their sons and daughters fail to promptly return phone calls, or when their spouses don't provide stimulating conversation, they can be devastated."

The introduction seemed to resonate with a woman whose voice I'd already learned to associate with Rachel – one of the corporate executives. "So, what you're saying is, their sense of worth, as well as their satisfaction with life, is tied to the responses they get, or don't, from their kids or their spouses. Good luck!"

"Exactly." Eleanor said. "And, the old saying, 'We can't go home again,' really applies here. Seriously, I'm passionate about this, because I believe that aging and the 'golden years' are terribly devalued in our

youth-oriented culture. In other cultures, and at other times, older persons were respected and honored for their wisdom and experience. I'd like to encourage women to see themselves as continuing to evolve, creating new opportunities for themselves — regardless of their ages. I'm angry at all the hype about 'anti-aging.' Instead, I'd like to promote aging with joy and respect."

Rachel seemed invigorated by that and added, "I think what you're saying is that many of us may be guilty of living on automatic pilot, and it's so important at this juncture to stop doing that. When we were young, we probably lived as if we had limitless time. Many of us were assigned — or chose — roles that were similar to the ones our mothers or grandmothers had."

"I like to think of it this way," Rachel continued. "Compare 'youth' to standing on the bridge of time and watching the water — the days and even years — flowing by. This flow of resources seems limitless. We probably all spent enormous time *killing* time — living in patterns that formed almost of themselves, and we were probably not even conscious of our parts in those patterns."

There was a murmur of agreement around the table.

"So," Rachel concluded, "at this stage of our lives, we know that life is finite. Even though we have more time than grandma did, we need to face the fact that lifetimes have limits and that we are in the final years. It becomes terribly important to take ourselves off automatic pilot — to consider and reconsider who we are now, who we want to be and what attributes and resources we have."

I was intrigued when I heard the next response from a quiet voice I associated with Kelly. During the introductions, she had stressed the importance of family in her life, and I felt an instant connection with her. She said, "This is all starting to make sense to me. Somewhere along the line, I told myself I don't want the next forty-five years of my life to be like the last forty-five. Not that there was anything wrong with those years; I was happily married, I had children, and I had a good life. But I was bound by tradition. Now I want to change the rhythm. Can someone really do that?"

"Yes," Eleanor responded. "It seems that one step toward having a fulfilling life is to enhance our awareness of where we are *right now* – to get off automatic pilot."

Susan, whose quiet but organized introduction had the paradoxical effect of making her a standout, asked to summarize what she'd heard so far. "So, as I understand it, some women get stuck in old roles that no longer work. Then, these women may become dissatisfied with life – maybe even depressed – possibly blaming others for not making them happy. And, they're not stepping back to see that they need to become part of the solution by changing direction or focus."

"That's exactly right," Eleanor said. "And our changes may be major. What's more, we will probably have to be extremely creative, because the old guidebooks – I like to say the old recipe books – don't even have pages for us."

"Hmm, so we have to create our own pages," suggested Laura.

"Now, I'm getting what you're after, Eleanor," said Kelly. "Although I hadn't met some of you before today, I do know a few of you well, and I know that you have created new pages for yourselves instead of trying to re-cycle through your old guidebooks. Is it your idea, Eleanor, to discuss how we've done that and record what we have learned to share with others? So, does that make us the new 'Pages'?"

Rachel promptly spoke up, "Count me in if we're going to be honest about our experiences. It's not only about the positive things we've done and learned; but we also need to talk about the obstacles we've met and maybe some failures, too. I frequently say I've had at least six different lifetimes – not reincarnations, mind you, like a Shirley MacLaine – just different lifetimes. And, often, things I learned in one lifetime – even when those weren't happy experiences – helped me succeed in the next lifetime."

In contrast to Rachel's apparent eagerness, Susan quietly asked again for clarification. "Before I commit to this project, I need to understand our purpose. Is our goal to write a self-help book for women — sort of like, *How to Achieve a More Satisfying Life*?"

"Whoa!" responded Ellen, in what sounded like good humor. "Most of the time, I have more questions than answers. Years of helping clients find careers to match their skills and personalities have clearly shown me that we must ask the right questions before we can find the right answers."

"Well, I thought I did ask the right question, Ellen," Susan said and laughed. "Now, let's discuss the answer."

"Right," chimed in Laura. "I suspect women have had enough books and lists telling them how to do this and how to do that, especially if the advice comes from people who never did those things themselves. I think it could be more helpful to offer women the questions we've asked and are still asking ourselves. We can talk about our struggles with difficult issues and then describe our honest responses, even if we know they're not perfect."

"May I say that this sounds like a rather challenging task? I don't for a minute doubt that the women around this table have enormous wisdom to share, but we need to get the material organized. Consider just trying to follow our conversation for the past half-hour," Susan quipped.

"Right," Kelly agreed. "We need someone who is *really* organized to take notes."

Suddenly the room echoed with women calling out, "Kelly! Kelly!"

"Oh, Kelly," Ellen said, "don't you remember the first rule about meetings? Never let yourself become the answer to your own question. But you know that you'd be perfect for that role."

"Okay," said Eleanor. "I'm assuming that y'all are joining me in this venture. I heartily agree with both the idea of our keeping notes and with Kelly acting as our Chief in Charge of Summarization. But let's take it a step further. Let's commit ourselves, at each session's conclusion, to come up with three to five of the most important ideas or points we believe could prove helpful to others. That way, by the time we work through the topics we think are most significant, we'll have a record of what we've said — a great new recipe book, if you will. And we'll pledge to include, along with the recipes we believe will work, an honest account of those that have resulted in nothing more than a pile of crumbs."

The general murmur of agreement that followed included a few jibes about Kelly's needing a supply of headache medicine to cope with the bouncing ball of conversation, and someone commented, "Well, at least, since we're all women, you're not the one in the room voted most likely to bring the cookies."

"Okay," announced Eleanor, "it's time to call this introductory meeting to a close. Thanks to each of you for coming and hearing me out on this project. We'll meet again in one week and get to work on more of the specifics. I hope everyone feels comfortable talking candidly about all kinds of issues and honestly relating your own experiences. What we've agreed on is the world we live in today is very different from the one experienced by most of our female mentors. We believe it's very important to share the realities of being an older woman in today's world, because there are thousands of women, like us, who need new patterns for aging and living well."

"Agreed!"

~

And just like that, they were gone. I went back to my own work, determined to find a better spot before I had to endure another interruption in the few precious hours I had available for writing my thesis.

During the week, though, I kept thinking about "my women" and wondering about their personal stories. Just as their words and phrases had penetrated my perfect work space, bits and pieces of their discussions occupied space in my brain, and I caught myself ruminating often on what I had overheard.

As the days passed, I began to look forward to the "interruption"; I craved it, really. I had been hooked, and I had the premonition that eavesdropping on these women, as they candidly talked about their lives, would be as rewarding as it had been entertaining.

Sure enough, the next time they met, I was next to the wall, books all around, fingers on my keyboard, and ears tuned to the conversation. Over the weeks I learned their routine: every Thursday at 9:30 A.M., enter by the side door, chit-chat about things for a while and then delve into serious issues — interrupted often by easy laughter. And then, after ninety minutes, silence. They were gone again until the next Thursday.

During the months of their meetings, I finished my thesis: "The Image of the Outsider in the Works of Canadian Women Authors," which was unread by anyone except my professor and useful to no known purpose in the universe except to secure my degree, which led to a job.

Meanwhile, the real learning had come from eavesdropping.

When Did I
Stop Dancing?

Making choices

I came to recognize the typical pattern of the meetings. There would be some casual conversation and catching up before Eleanor asked the group to focus on the formal discussion of a particular topic. Today, though, she seemed a bit agitated, very unlike her usual demeanor. Well, at least the demeanor that I *thought* was her usual demeanor. I was already finding it hard to imagine that "my women," my sages, could be anything other than what they were when I was eavesdropping.

~

"I'm so frustrated," Eleanor said with a sigh, "I've just come from my office, and once again, I'm working with a woman who seems to have everything, and, yet, she's both anxious and sad — and clueless when I ask about goals and plans. I think earlier generations of women knew what to do with their lives — perhaps because they didn't live as long and certainly had fewer options open to them. Now, women like the one I worked with today, lack confidence to begin anything new of any significance. They keep clinging to their old roles, which often results in their being dissatisfied and their families getting annoyed and frustrated.

"I have been surprised to learn how many hours some of them spend just playing golf or tennis — both wonderful sports — but the problem is that *playing* is just about all they do. Their lives revolve around whether or not they've been included in a league, and, of course, that depends on abilities that typically decrease with age.

"Other women tell me about repeated trips to plastic surgeons. They've been lifted, altered, injected with Botox, etc., in their quests to look youthful — which I see, again, as conscious or unconscious attempts to return to earlier roles. You were invited to this group specifically because you haven't chosen those paths. Can you tell me, what do you know that eludes the others?"

"I once had a mentor," Ellen eagerly said, "who called my attention to a simple fact. You don't say, 'I am walking on my right foot or my wrong foot.' You say, 'I'm walking on my right foot or my left foot.' Why is it, do you think, that we immediately jump to a conclusion about whether we're living our lives the *right* way or the *wrong* way — as though there's only *one* way? I like to think my life is constantly self-correcting, not because things are wrong, but because I need to do something differently."

"Ah," said Rachel, knowingly," but sometimes an opportunity comes along that you might or might not take, and it depends on what's happening in your life."

"Don't you think that's where real friends come in?" Ellen asked. "Like you, Rachel. You will always tell me the truth whether I want to hear it or not. Then it's up to me to decide whether I'm self-correcting or running to the edge of the cliff."

That comment elicited laughter and good natured kidding of Rachel.

"But, Ellen," Susan said, pausing for the group to get serious again, "it's easy to tell you the truth because you're so *open* to hearing it. You never seem to hold grudges or make negative assumptions about someone's intentions. I personally like to think that every day can be an opportunity to learn, if we're open to it, and I think you are a good example of someone who does that!"

Kelly agreed with the importance of friends who tell you the truth. "But I want to get back to the fundamentals in my life," she said. "Not change, really. More like a re-connection. Like someone is asking me, 'When did you stop dancing?' and I have to think back to whether I ever liked to dance in the first place, or whether it's something I really *loved* and want to do again."

"Hmm, I like that dancing image," Ellen said. "It reminds me of a seminar I went to. You know the ones: for 'women of a certain age,' during which someone tries to convince us to buy something or invest with someone. The group leader was a man who probably had the best of intentions, but he wanted to provide answers rather than acknowledge our questions, especially about what we want to do with the time we have left. He was very enthusiastic about everyone trying tap dancing. To him, I suppose, it seemed as though it was the wildest activity any one of us could imagine."

"Obviously, he never met Ellen, just back from an African safari," Eleanor quipped.

Ellen shot back, "Right, or Rachel, who came close to being arrested, as I understand it, in a protest over one of her worthy causes."

"I was perfectly innocent," Rachel commented. "And correct, too."

"Anyway, back to the tap dancing," said Ellen. "So he concluded the seminar by telling us all to go out that very week and sign up for tap dancing lessons. How silly. And how out of touch! I love to watch really good tap dancing, and I've even been known to tap a bit around the kitchen. I admire women who join dance troupes at 70 and keep tapping until they're past 80. But we have to move beyond the position where we make our choices based on what *others* think we should do. Tap dance, if you want, or don't tap dance — if that's *your* preference."

"Broaden your horizons," Eleanor said. "I think that's what I'm hearing. Finally, with children raised and professional lives completed or nearing completion, we need to decide *which* dance we want to do."

This topic stirred up lively comments around the group.

Susan whispered, "Or if we want to dance at all."

Laura chuckled as she added, "Personally, I'm thinking about tango lessons."

"You know, while my husband might enjoy my arriving home in a luscious tango outfit, I'm not necessarily as adventurous about dancing as the rest of you," said Susan, who sounded like she was smiling. "But, dancing decisions aside, I wholeheartedly, emphatically believe in the idea of making one's *own* choices. If not now — when?"

"Susan, I'm definitely in agreement with you," Eleanor said, "and the message we want to get across to others — whenever and wherever we get the chance — is that specific choices aside, it's the *choosing* that matters. I *choose* to be very involved with volunteer work having to do with making policy — not cookies. It makes me happy, and it's my choice. A woman who *chooses* to take up residence in a village in Africa and teach women to sew is, hopefully, making the right choice for herself. And the woman who *chooses* to make frilly dresses for her granddaughters has the right to that choice, as well."

"Thank you for that," said Kelly. "Do you remember the first time someone said to you, 'Well, what do you want to do now?' For me, it didn't happen until just a few years ago, and I panicked. What do you mean, 'What do I want to do now'? How should I know? For decades, what I *needed* to do occupied more time than I had, so it was never necessary to pose the question. It was terribly uncomfortable for me to cope with the idea that I had options and that I needed to make choices. If we're going to be perfectly honest about all this, I feel quite intimidated by women who suddenly take up white water rafting or start a small business creating art from found objects or whatever," she added. "That's not me. Why do I need to make choices like that?"

"Ah," Laura acknowledged, "once again we're back to the importance of *choosing*, not the importance of the specific choices, don't you think? Here's where our message might resound the loudest. Our advice is not, as some books or gurus might give, to make a *particular* choice. We're not going to advise someone to take up residence at an ashram. Our message is: *choose for yourself.* As long as that choice fits you, doesn't harm you or others, and doesn't deny your true self, it's the right choice for you."

"Too bad there isn't a manual of choices a woman could look at," Ellen said, "like a Chinese menu for those moments when she can't get past the panic of knowing she's free to choose."

Count on Susan, I learned, to have a book that fits the topic.

She said, "Decades ago, I read a fabulous book, called *Gifts of Age*, and I remember thinking, *Wow, it must be great to be seventy or eighty*, because of the admirable people who were interviewed for the book. I was encouraged by the diverse role models. They seemed so wise. And I wondered why I, or anyone else, couldn't become just like those people: knowledgeable, interesting and fully involved in life."

"Well, then," Kelly said, "I have a question about wisdom. How do we acquire wisdom so we can make wise choices? Is it just the result of getting older? Is it about carrying our past with us and learning from it?"

"It's exposure to wise people," Rachel declared. "Time spent with wise people is more valuable than a library of books. You can get gems about living well from people for whom you have regard. It's like cross-fertilization."

"I agree," added Susan. "Consciously seeking out the company of wise people, with proven good instincts, should be a goal for any discerning woman."

"Also, I don't think wisdom is something that's ever *done*, ever *completed*, ever something that you've *got*. I think it's something that *grows*. It's about openness, don't you agree?" Eleanor asked.

"Language becomes really important, too, when we think about being wise," Laura said. "What we *say* is meaningful. For example, when the neighbors' kids come to visit and are just wild, I could say, 'These kids are driving me nuts!' or I could say, 'I'm not having fun. I need to leave the room or send them home now.' I can talk myself into being wise, or I can view the situation in such a way that I become furious."

"That's such an important comment and still consistent with our topic of choices," Susan said. "I'm reminded of the wise advice I heard from an author who spoke at the Miami Book Fair. He told members of the audience, 'Consider carefully what you think and say, because how you think becomes your behavior, and your behavior becomes who you are.' "

"Well, I'm reading a book, too," Rachel said. "It describes negative thoughts as *enemy* thoughts. Sometimes, when my family asks me what I'm doing, I tell them that I'm having enemy thoughts, and these enemy thoughts may be destructive to them, to me or to everybody within my reach. With just the right tone to my voice, they understand that it's in their own self-interest to keep out of the way."

The other women responded at once with hearty laughter.

"I'll have to remember that one. 'Enemy thoughts.' Although I don't think I could say it without laughing," Laura finally said.

Eleanor gently nudged them back to the discussion. "We always have movies playing in our heads about what should be happening, why something has happened, or why someone else acted in a way we didn't like. I've read a lot recently about how *mindful attention* contributes to wisdom.

"It comes down to obeying the rules we learned in elementary school: 'Stop. Look. Listen.' If we want to live effectively, we need to stop: take time everyday to get away from all the noise and get quiet. Then, look and listen — pay attention to our own inner dialogues. It's important for each of us to ask ourselves, 'What do I want? What am I thinking and feeling right now?' Without this mindful attention we may be expending lots of energy on repetitive, ineffective behaviors — like walking on a treadmill, which takes lots of energy but doesn't get us anywhere new."

"So, what I've heard," said Rachel, "in our discussion of wisdom is that we need wise people in our lives, we need to pay attention each day to ourselves, and we need to remember what we've learned from the past — from both positive and negative experiences.

"You always bring things with you from the past," she continued. "I wrote a memoir for my granddaughter, and I hesitated about what I should include. Should I tell her the story of how I was engaged to another man when I met the man who was to become her grandfather? Tell her that, even though I had second thoughts and was uncertain, I married the man I was engaged to? I knew immediately after the wedding ceremony that I'd made a mistake. Can you believe I called my future husband from my wedding reception and told him we should have run away together? It took me a year, but I got that first marriage annulled. Then I married the man I truly loved, and we were together for forty-five years."

"You called from the wedding reception? Really?" Ellen asked, not masking her obvious astonishment.

"My granddaughter loved the story," Rachel said. "She thought it was the most romantic thing. I taught her that very little in life is irreversible. That's an important message."

"Did you remember to send back all the wedding gifts, Rachel?" Susan asked.

The group erupted into laughter.

"Did we get anywhere today with our topic — that of *making wise choices*?" Eleanor asked. "Our time is almost up, and I wonder if we have enough notes for Kelly's summary. Maybe our topics need to be less broad. We took up the whole subject of *choice*, and perhaps next time we need to be more focused."

"Well, if we don't want this book to be longer than *War and Peace* or less useful than a grocery list," Laura said, "we do need more organization to our conversations. But I think there are enough important messages from this session to record:

- The choices you make for yourself are important.

- The act of choosing is, in itself, important — perhaps as important as the specific choices.

- Be mindful of what matters to you. Especially at this stage in your life, it really is about you.

- This is not a manual of right or wrong choices; look around at others, but most importantly, look within yourself.

- Dance. Or don't dance. You choose."

∽

Oh, no! Time was up, and they were leaving me again. *Wait, talk some more about making choices in one's life*, I thought. I wanted to hear more about reversible and irreversible decisions. Did it take the indomitable will of Rachel to self-correct? Or was Ellen right? Could we think of changes in our lives as "self-corrections" instead of taking on the guilt that came from characterizing our lives as "wrong"? Could

Kelly, who had more questions than answers, figure out that she could dance if she wanted to — or not, if she didn't?

There I was, in a library, working on a paper that seemed more and more irrelevant, as I thought of my own life's direction. I thought I was moving forward on the correct path, having spent time on a side rail to have children and raise a family. Maybe that wasn't a side rail; maybe that was the main road.

As family demands lessened, I found myself both delighted and panicked. I realized I could decide what to do with my mornings — if not with my whole life. Was I doing what I *wanted* to do? Did I *want* to dance? *Was I dancing already?*

"Mindfulness" seemed to be the message with which the women had left me — to pay attention to my own questions and answers. I would have rather listened to *them*, but they were telling me to listen to *myself*.

But It Was Only a Lamp!

Navigating a sea of relationships

They threw back their heads and laughed heartily. At least that's the way I pictured the women as they began this morning's discussion — enjoying a good laugh at themselves, at each other, at life.

The chosen topic for today: *ways to effectively handle changes in important relationships*. Their ability to laugh at that, and other serious topics, prompted me to reflect. Thanks to modern medicine, we function reasonably well with replacement body parts; but, as I'm learning from these wise women, a healthy sense of humor is irreplaceable, especially when it comes to relationships.

∾

As usual, Eleanor started the formal discussion. "Although it may sound like I'm deviating from our theme . . . something I've never been known to do . . ."

Friendly laughter interrupted.

"All right," Eleanor admitted, "I tell my husband that's just the way Southerners talk. We *embroider* our stories. Anyway, as I was about to say: It's gratifying for me to see how we're bonding as a group — enjoying ourselves, even while tackling serious — often personally painful — subjects. I think the time is right for us to share more about ourselves with each other — to add depth to what we already know or have surmised. So, I'd like for each of you to include in today's discussion some information about your personality traits and how you think they've affected your life and your relationships."

"By 'personality traits', do you mean what we learned through the interesting assessment Ellen went over with us after our meeting last week?" asked Laura.

"Exactly," Eleanor said. "Thanks. The assessment you took was the Myers-Briggs Type Indicator, which Ellen is trained to administer. We thought our group dynamics — which are already good — could only be enhanced by a deeper understanding of each other's personality preferences. When we understand that such preferences differ from person to person, we can, hopefully, interact more effectively with people who might otherwise confuse or even annoy, us.

"Consider how our relationships within this group are evolving. Some of us weren't even acquainted before we started. As we share intimate information, as our relationships change — for better or worse — it is bound to create tension. We don't always agree on solutions and strategies. How do you handle the resulting tension now? Is it different from ways you have acted in the past? Our topic today is about meeting relationship challenges, and I'm looking forward to hearing how you've met those challenges in your lives."

∽

As the members told about themselves, I wrote feverishly, trying not to miss anything important. Rachel, of course, led the way. I could picture her as a young Girl Scout at the head of the pack. Their stories were like rich tapestries of varying colors and hues: some were funny, others tragic; they included failures as well as accomplishments.

They spoke of loves and losses and about fulfilling roles and responsibilities. Sometimes, with pride in their voices, they spoke of rebelling from expectations. They described how they dealt with changes that were thrust upon them, rather than being *chosen* by them, and how they met those challenges.

I was impressed by Kelly, who talked about her life today almost as if it were a re-birth. She'd been a homemaker, supporting her husband's career and then caring for him through his final, long illness. Her time and attention had been devoted to activities they enjoyed as a couple. After his death, she quietly reflected on her individual interests. She let go of places, people and things that took her time and that no longer held her interest. Instead, she pursued her love of art and began painting. Apparently, she was starting a small business venture with her watercolors.

I recalled from an earlier meeting that several of the women had enjoyed professional successes. I was impressed to learn that one had actually been a pioneer for women in corporate America, rising to become the first female vice president of a large (billion dollar) national corporation. Another had been the chief financial officer for an innovative design firm, and one of them spoke of her exciting job as a human resources director traveling to field offices in 33 states. I smiled when I heard another describe her accomplishment of becoming the first female vice president of a major retail chain and, in the next breath, tell of success and fun as an actress in local theater productions. Women of my generation take it for granted that there will be ample opportunities for advancement within our professions; yet, on the other side of the wall were women who were among the trailblazers for us to have those opportunities.

I felt buoyed by such good company and encouraged to complete the final steps toward attaining my master's degree. Many of the women earned both undergraduate and graduate degrees while married, working and raising children. One hadn't had time to complete her degree until age seventy!

Despite their extensive professional, cultural and educational accomplishments, it was obvious that their families and personal relationships were foremost in importance to them. They spoke of joyful celebrations, important milestones and of revered special mentors. They spoke quietly and sadly of losing parents, siblings, spouses – and most grievous of all – the deaths of children.

As Eleanor had prompted them to do, they talked about their personality traits. As I heard the descriptions I identified most readily with the introverts in the group, those who relish their time alone to 'recharge' their emotional energy. I suppressed a giggle when I realized how much I enjoyed eavesdropping. Mother would never have condoned such behavior. Well, hopefully, I could be forgiven. Eavesdropping allowed me to be apart from – and yet a part of – such interesting dialogue.

Some of the women described themselves as extroverts – no surprise there; but it was interesting to learn from their stories how extroverted behaviors can result in significant problems. I'd assumed that extroverts easily mastered relationships and that they interacted with others comfortably, even effortlessly.

What amazed me most, however, as I tried to absorb the many highlights of their collective histories, was how the women persisted through the changes in their lives and roles, re-inventing themselves when necessary. They were fully engaged with life; they remained interested and interesting. Some of them were still working, at least part time, or were so committed to volunteer work that I couldn't imagine them able to meet all their obligations. Several were actively involved in sports and physical fitness programs. Two of them were avid hikers and kayakers.

As was typical of the group, poignant tales were often followed by humorous ones, and so it was when Susan told the group that, work and education accomplishments aside, she was most excited about retirement and the opportunities to travel and be with her family. She added – to the obvious amazement of some in the group – that one of her favorite activities was playing poker. It seemed she learned the game from her older brother when they were young. Apparently, his allowance was regularly withheld because of some misdeed or other, and he played poker with Susan to win her allowance and restore his pocket change. Susan laughed happily and said it was "out of necessity" that she had become good at poker and that she continued to enjoy the risks and strategies required by the game.

When the last biography was completed, there was silence for a minute — unusual for this group. I imagined they were feeling many emotions and reflecting on what they had heard, just as I was doing.

∼

"Thank you for those wonderful stories," said Eleanor. "I certainly feel that we know each other better now. From your stories it is obvious that, as you matured and changed, your relationships also evolved. For example, your children grew up, left home and started their own families."

"Thank goodness," interjected Rachel, who had been quiet for a while. "They've given us precious grandchildren. There will be new relationships to add spice to our lives."

"Exactly," responded Eleanor. "As you see, we have now returned to our topic: how to interact effectively with important people in our lives as *we* change and as *they* do. Even positive changes in relationships often result in tension, if not conflict. So, I think this topic is particularly important for us at this stage of life."

"I'm still trying to understand how personality traits are related to our relationships," said Kelly, "but I think Susan's story about her interactions with her brother was helpful."

"What do you mean, Kelly?" asked Susan. "This sounds interesting."

"Well, Susan, it sounds like you interacted with your brother much as I've seen you interact with us. You don't make a big show of it, but you quietly sit back and assess. Then you question something or see something from a different perspective. And you persist until you've been heard."

"I'd say that, in the case of her brother, she came, she saw and she conquered — the game!" exclaimed Laura.

Kelly continued, asking, "So, are these personality traits, like 'Introversion' and 'Extroversion', things we're just stuck with from birth and can't ever change?"

Ellen answered, "Sorry, friends, I can see that it's hard for you to accept, but these traits *are* pretty stable. I'd prefer not to think of being 'stuck' with being introverted – or extroverted. It is simply who I am. However, I can learn strategies to succeed at activities and in relationships using my strengths, and being aware of areas where my personality type will be challenged."

Susan sounded as if she were smiling when she said to Kelly, "It seems to me that you and I share some traits. Like you, I am organized and somewhat introverted. But, if I had to give a party for twenty-five people, as you are doing next week, I'd have a total breakdown – not just a nervous reaction, I tell you – a breakdown! How in the world are you doing that?"

Kelly quickly agreed, "Yes, I see those similarities, too. I prefer supporting and guiding from behind the scenes, especially with volunteer activities, and I love my quiet times when I can paint. I guess, just as Ellen suggested, the strategies I learned in the past – to help others accomplish their goals – are still with me today. The skills I acquired then help me now, as I navigate through uncomfortable places, to seek my own goals."

"I can certainly see our varying personality styles as I listen to our stories and conversations," commented Laura. "But in spite of our differences, we all seem to get along. So, why, Eleanor, do you say they could cause problems in intimate relationships?"

Ellen jumped in, "Oh, I have such a good response to that question. I married 'Mr. Fun,' as many of you know. Phil loved spontaneity, and everyone loved him for it. Me, too. But I love to plan and organize my activities – even those that are just for fun. When Phil retired, it drove me crazy that his pattern was to sit back until noon and then decide what *he* wanted to do that day – and, of course, what he wanted *me* to do with him.

"One day I decided to be just plain old stubborn and not budge an inch all morning. I sat there, miserable, with my hands folded, waiting for him. Sure enough, at noon he went into motion, and we had a great, fun day. We finally agreed on a compromise: each of us got to be in charge of a portion of our days together. I could enjoy my planned activities and let go, or at least postpone, my preference for structure to join him in spontaneous fun. I think we found a win-win solution to fit our very different personality styles. I'm so thankful we worked through that and enjoyed the time together before his sudden death. How terrible it would have been if we hadn't considered and understood our personality differences and, instead, had spent that time being irritated with each other."

Rachel countered, "Well, I'm glad you were able to compromise so effectively, Ellen. I'm sure some of my conflicts in relationships have to do with my independent, risk-taking personality traits."

"Do I detect as much pleasure in your voice as regret, Rachel?" asked Laura. "Remind us please, Ellen, what did you say Rachel's type came into the world with?"

"Combat booties!" Ellen responded.

"Right, combat booties!" they all shouted.

"Well," said Rachel, "at least I can joke about myself. When I married as a young woman, I went into it battling for independence. I was a professional woman, responsible for eight different facilities from Long Island to the Bronx. Yet, my husband didn't want me to get in the car if it snowed. I would get furious with him. I felt it was my right to go to work regardless of the weather."

"Do you think," Ellen asked, "that it was his *right* to be protective?"

"No," said Rachel, battling still. "Although maybe he was simply behaving as he had been *taught*, feeling he was *supposed* to protect me. Or maybe he felt a little guilty if he was at home when I was at work."

Eleanor said, thoughtfully, "This discussion is stirring up some old memories that are really intriguing for me, and I'll bet I'll think about it again and again. Like you, Rachel, I was also independent and self-reliant. In fact, my parents talked about that characteristic often — most of the time positively. And when I began dating my high school sweetheart, I was that self-reliant person. However, when we married one year out of high school, somehow I naively, and apparently unconsciously, *assumed* that he would become the protective breadwinner and I would be the Southern housewife, armed with my *Betty Crocker Cookbook* and ruffled apron. In other words, we'd just slip into the stereotypical roles for husbands and wives in those days."

"I can't even imagine that," chimed in Laura and Kelly.

"Well, it's true," Eleanor continued. "When my husband didn't play his role according to my script and instead continued his young male activities like working on fast cars, he often wasn't available to me. We got into a sort of marital tug-of-war with no discussion of the deeper issues. I wonder how different it might have been if we had understood each other's traits and preferences – as Ellen and Phil did – and worked through them. We remained friends, by the way, long after our divorce, and we talked about many things, but this subject never came up, and I regret that it can't now, since he died several years ago."

"So, did you just keep trying to depend on him until the bitter end?" asked Laura.

"No, I finally began using my skills from childhood and became more self-reliant. In fact, I'm thankful that he inadvertently facilitated that part of me, which I value today."

"Well, I'm now married again, having been a widow for some time," Rachel continued, "and I'm fighting for independence again. And, like you, Eleanor, I've changed some over the years. I've become more appreciative of the help of others, but I'm still resistant when I feel my independence is being threatened. For example, I went to the lamp store the other day and bought a lamp, and my husband was surprised that I would just make the decision and buy the lamp. Imagine! As if I needed help to buy a lamp! Then, he insisted that he would assemble the lamp, even though I felt sure he didn't know how. I think of myself as being more mechanical than he is, but he really wanted to do it. I figured that my watching him would only add pressure, so I left for a meeting. I did ask him to just leave the lamp alone and make the lunch he had promised me."

Ellen said, "It sounds like he wanted to be Daddy."

Kelly thoughtfully added, "Or, he was just being very traditional."

"I probably would have just given him the lamp and let him figure it out on his own," said Ellen.

"Well, that's what I did," Rachel replied. "My first husband and I elevated marital bickering to an art form, which I thought was great. My children now tell me they hated it, but I just saw it as spirited discussion. So I'm trying now, in this marriage, to avoid sulking and not say punishing things when he does something that I think makes no sense."

"But it's only a lamp!" Ellen said kiddingly.

"Yes," said Rachel, "but we are who we are."

Kelly gently countered, "We do tend to fight over stupid things."

"Yes," Eleanor agreed, "but sometimes the object of the fight isn't as stupid as it seems. We're probably not fighting as much about lamps, as we are our rights to exercise *our own* judgments, based upon our own personality traits, and hold onto power over *our own* decisions."

"And not only that," Rachel said, "he didn't have lunch ready when I got back!"

Laughter almost drowned out Rachel's final comment.

"But I love the guy!"

When they stopped laughing enough for me to hear again, Susan was talking.

"Before we end today, I'd like to read something that is important to me, and I think it's relevant to our discussion. These two points are from a book I just finished, *Crones Don't Whine*, by Jean Shinoda Bolen. The first point is that we should trust our instincts because they become sharper as we grow older and wiser. The second point is that we should understand and remember that silence is interpreted by others as consent."

"So, you're saying silence isn't *always* golden, as is often quoted, and that we *shouldn't* stifle our objections," Laura commented.

"Exactly. It's important to speak up when the truth should be heard. I wish I'd understood that long ago; I could have benefited from that wisdom many times. One can speak compassionately – even fiercely – or quietly, depending on the circumstances. Of course, listening carefully and thoughtfully to other points of view is also important; however, it's important to speak up when we disagree with what is said or done."

"Thank you for those points, Susan. I've jotted them down for myself," said Ellen. "And *I'd* like to add a couple of thoughts, too. I believe it's often important, maybe essential, to leave regrets behind and not fight old battles. Above all, enjoy life. Life is difficult, but we can find ways to cope. I heard this over and over again in our stories."

"Resiliency, resiliency," they all chimed in.

"And," Eleanor said, "overall, people do make it."

"Overall," a few said briskly.

"Overall," a few said wistfully.

"It's time to go," said Eleanor, "and we've covered a lot of ground today. What key points do we want to record?"

"I've listed some wonderful adjectives I've heard today," Ellen said. "I think they describe someone built to last:

- Resilient

- Adaptable

- Accommodating

- Balanced

- Grounded in Values"

~

And they were off again, doing all the things they did when I was not there to eavesdrop on their lives and thoughts. I was left with a song fragment in my brain about knowing when to hold 'em. Yes, and when to fold 'em. That certainly seemed to be an essential part of wisdom. My women (I did think of them now as "mine") had given me a standard for knowing when to hold and when to fold – when to yield. Sometimes, when your personhood or an important principle is at stake – you've got to hold 'em.

But, a wise person knows when it's really only a lamp!

You Never Know
Where Sex Will Take You.

Late-life coupling

S ex. That's the issue the women started with, introduced by Laura, who wasn't saying for sure whether this was an urgent issue in her life right now or whether, as a widow of several years, she was just getting ready for a new step.

The topic helped to jar me out of my disgruntled mood, brought on by the contrast between the sparkling sunny day at my doorstep and the black cloud over my morning preparations for school and work. It was one of those "lost" days: the kids lost their gloves, my husband lost his car keys, and I lost my temper.

Younger students, having only themselves to consider, could approach their thesis work with order and equanimity. I approached it with peanut butter on my notes and another form to fill out for an elementary school fund-raiser. Sex? Definitely a luxury in our busy household. My curiosity was piqued.

~

"It's been a very long time since I was a young woman dating the man I eventually married, and he was the only man I ever had sex with," Laura said. "I can't even imagine approaching this subject with a man now."

Ellen said she was a virgin when she married, and she, too, had never had a sexual relationship with anyone other than her husband. "I've thought about starting new relationships since Phil's death," she said, "but I really haven't thought about the sexual aspect of a new relationship."

"Well," said Kelly, "relationships may start platonically, but if you see a person long enough, typically the relationship will become more intimate."

"Sometimes it seems that men just want to go to bed," Susan declared with such firmness that the other women started to laugh uproariously. "Wait, wait," she said. "I only know this from talking with other women."

"And in those books you read."

More laughter.

"Remember how the 'sexual revolution' was supposed to remove all the prohibitions our parents had about sex, so we could be honest and forthright?" Susan continued. "But we had no context for even discussing sex, or our sexual appetites and preferences."

Rachel's voice was firm. "I never had any problem discussing sex with my husbands," she insisted.

"Yes," Ellen said, "but that's you, Rachel. You must have a very valuable genetic pre-disposition to honesty and forthrightness, but I don't think the rest of us have that same comfort level."

"I grant you," Rachel said, "that it was never a part of the education and training of young women to know about or speak about sex. Most of us were blissfully uninformed, and, for some of us, that created problems within our marriages. We didn't even understand how we were feeling or even know what we wanted from our husbands."

"Right," Kelly added. "Even now, it feels as though we ought to get permission from someone — I don't know from whom — our parents, the men in our lives, society as a whole, to be talking frankly among ourselves about sex. I feel sure my daughter doesn't feel this way, but she didn't get that freedom from me!"

There were murmurs of agreement.

Susan reminded everyone of a recent article about the increase of sexually transmitted diseases among the elderly. "Life is much more complicated now, for all of its freedom," she said. "When we were young, it was simpler — in a way. We met a man, we fell in love and we married. Now, we have to worry about exchanging sexual histories with these significant men."

Eleanor said, "You know it's not in my nature to be dogmatic, but I strongly urge my female clients to protect themselves. A woman must ask about a man's sexual history, and she must be willing to share her own. She should demand that a man use a condom until she is confident that sex with him is safe, because it might truly be her life on the line. The world has changed, and when our health and the health of our partners may be at stake, we can't be deterred for fear of hurting someone's feelings."

"Well, it's certainly not simple at our age," Kelly said. "Physically, we've changed. How do you get past that? I'm sure there must be ways to meet these challenges — maybe with the help of our gynecologists."

"Oh, lord," Laura said and sighed, "it's like being a teenager all over again. How do you look? How do you perform? Constantly questioning yourself."

"I've learned," Eleanor said, "from my formal education, and informally from men's conversations, that many men continue to be sexual until they die. I recall hearing one guy bragging that he's the only single man in his condo complex, and he was boasting of being in demand! Older women who date need to be aware of these things and must protect themselves."

"Of course, maybe he *thought* he was the only available man and was being pursued by all of the women," Susan said. "I hear stories about women pursuing the plumber, the repair man, the landscaper. How come I've never met any women who would fit a description like that? Is it just a male fantasy?"

"That's a good question to explore," Laura said. "The common stereotype is that older women are no longer interested in sex, if they ever were, and that men past a certain age are too feeble. Take a look at movies that show older couples. If there is any suggestion of a sexual aspect to the relationship, it's often made fun of."

"Have you noticed the number of ads on TV for men's sexual enhancement products?" Kelly asked. "I was mortified while watching an ad with my daughter and son-in-law early one evening to hear, 'And if an erection lasts more than four hours . . .' Really, how do you engage in conversation after that? But it certainly underscores the truth that men do not intend to let age or illnesses sideline them from intimacy."

"We may laugh or even cringe," said Rachel, "but let's be honest. As men age, they become very concerned with their own sexuality, even if they're not good at communicating those concerns. Women have to understand that, respect that and acknowledge that appropriate medications or marital aids have their place. And they're not just for men. We may have been squeamish about using something to enhance our own physical response when we were young, but that was then. This is now. Get over it."

"I can tell you," Eleanor said, "that women have individual differences in their sexuality, just as they do in other aspects of their lives. Some women have even come to me concerned that their hormones might be out of balance because they were enjoying an increase in libido. Often these changes are related to being in love with a new partner, following the death of a spouse."

"Lucky new partner!" someone blurted out.

"Yes." Eleanor said. "Because women share so little about themselves in the area of sexual appetites, they question whether they are wrong to feel this way."

"I can understand that," Rachel added. "Perhaps, for whatever reason, a woman might not be completely fulfilled during her marriage. It's a cliché that 'it takes two', because it's so true. She could want the next man in her life to be very sexually active and she might be more responsive. Then, too, if the man is rekindling the sexual aspect of his own life after a hiatus — say, following the death of his spouse — the formula could be lively."

"This is going to be an interesting discussion to summarize," Kelly said, to general laughter. "Do we record that women are as sexual as men throughout their lives?"

"I think we should record," Laura said, "that women in general are capable of enjoying sexual intimacy as long as they live, and that, as in other aspects of their lives, individual differences apply. And that's okay."

"Since we are on a roll, I have a related question," Kelly said. "The first time you have sex with a man after the death of your partner, do you feel like you're cheating? Paul McCartney said in an interview that he felt that way after his wife Linda died."

"I have a friend," Ellen said, "who was so concerned about this issue that she discussed it with her grown son. She needed someone to support her decision to have sex again. I guess it seemed almost like a way for her deceased husband to give her permission to get on with her life."

Ellen's statement got quite a rise out of the group.

"I can't imagine going to my kids!" Kelly declared. "Maybe to tell them that I'm seeing someone, maybe a conversation, but never to ask permission to go away for the weekend with someone. But this topic makes me think about the kids' involvement. If there's someone new in your life, are your kids really concerned, or are they relieved?"

Ellen responded, "I think, ultimately, a woman has to make her own decisions about new relationships and not allow her children to make such decisions. I admit, though, that women should protect their children at the start of new relationships."

"When someone new comes into the family dynamic, there are always lots of questions," Eleanor said. "They range from who gets the jewelry, to where you'll live, to how you'll relate to each other's families and friends."

"Right," Ellen said, "there are lots of questions to explore. But say, how did we get here from sex?"

"You never know where sex is going to take you," Laura said.

In the laughter and verbal mayhem that followed, I lost the thread of the conversation for a bit until I heard Eleanor.

"Let's get our summary done before we forget the most important points, and we'll save a discussion about those other questions for another session. Kelly, please record these points:

- Women need to understand their own sexual needs and appetites, and to realize their needs and appetites may change over time.

- We live in a time that is different — more perilous — than what we knew as young women. Precautions like condoms and the exchange of personal sexual histories are absolutely necessary to protect both partners.

- Do what's comfortable and safe for you.

- Dating later in life is just as exciting, as nerve-rattling and as complicated as dating ever was. Just try to relax and enjoy it.

- Each woman must decide when a relationship is right for her. She may find less support from her children, or his, than she'd hoped for, as they struggle with the concept of their parents with new partners.

And I thought all that business about sexual history-taking would be over after marriage! Now, my women are talking about how to handle this sensitive issue with guys in their 70s, or older. The dating challenge all over again. The good news is that intimacy is not over after menopause. The bad news is that caution is still in order. A new love interest in later years had not entered my imagination. These women continue to amaze and amuse me.

The World Turned Upside Down.

Losses, lessons and liberation

Y ou can't appreciate spring fully unless you've had a winter. That thought had been running through my mind all morning because it was spring – a brilliant, dandelion kind of day when all shades of yellow and green appear as if by magic where yesterday there was only brown.

I was very tempted to play hooky from my dissertation and just luxuriate in the myriad greens and the warm sun. But I felt a "breaking through", the phenomenon that veteran Vermonters describe as the moment when the ice finally cracks on the river and the water starts to flow again. I felt a breakthrough in my writing, and I didn't want to waste it. Plus, of course, it was the day on which I was to eavesdrop on my women, and since I never knew what they'd say next, I didn't want to miss the conversation.

They, too, seem to have caught spring fever. There was a lot more buzz as they entered their room, and it took them longer than usual to settle into their formal discussion.

~

"Where's Laura?" someone asked.

The answer came from Eleanor. "She's coming, but she had to take her cat to the vet first. That poor cat is older than the hills, and Laura's spent a fortune on her – probably the equivalent of the gross national product of a small African country."

"I can understand that," Kelly said. "She loves that cat, and they have a shared history together. That matters a lot, particularly as we age. I'd be lost without my dogs. They give me unqualified love the moment I walk in my door, and I can tell them everything without fear they'll hold a grudge or think less of me. All I need to do for my share of the bargain is provide food, treats, walks and back rubs. I can't even calculate all I've spent on them, but I wouldn't trade them for the world."

"My husband says that he's at an age where the only animals he wants in the house are ones that are stuffed or made of china," said Susan. "I accuse him of being heartless, but I do understand. Pets require at least as much work as children and they're welcome in fewer places."

Laura burst into the room. "Tabby's going to be fine. Just a touch of a kidney infection, and I've already started her on antibiotics. I know some day I'll lose her, but I'm so glad it's not today! So what are we talking about? Catch me up."

"Cats, dogs and the economy of Africa," Rachel quipped.

"You know what I hear us talking about in a round-about way?" Eleanor asked. "Loss. Loss and the fear of loss. Some time ago we said this was an important topic that needed to be discussed. Let's go with it today."

"A very sensitive subject. Thank goodness the sun is shining today. If we start to get too emotional or morbid, I'm heading for the door," Kelly warned.

"I'm sorry that this is a painful topic, and we are mindful, Kelly, that the loss of your husband is recent. But it is such an important subject that we need to go forward with it, if that's agreeable with all of you," Eleanor continued.

"Thanks, Eleanor, "responded Kelly. "It is such an important subject for our book on issues of aging. It's inevitable that we're going to lose pets, friends, maybe a spouse, and God forbid a child or grandchild."

"Yes, personal loss, which of course can happen at any age. Do you know that Elizabeth Bishop poem about the art of losing, how it starts small with things like keys but ends up with the tragedy of someone we love?" Susan asked. "There really is an art to handling it. I'm thinking too of physical loss. My grandchild wanted me to skip with her. Skip? I've certainly lost skipping. I'm trying hard to hold onto walking!"

Her remark set off a buzz about physical ailments. Someone protested that she's fine; she plays golf several times a week with no significant problems. Oh yes, she admitted, that lump in her bag is her ibuprofen, the secret to her making it to the last hole. Others complained of arthritis, stiffness, loss of muscle tone from chin to the knee – the usual litany.

∾

What impressed me was their ability to laugh the whole time – rather than whine. *Maybe that's the secret,* I thought, while The Pages itemized their ills. While drugs can help, the real tonic is laughter. I've read academic research showing the positive effects of laughter – enhancing overall health, and I've even relied on a quote from it: a good belly laugh is worth fifteen minutes of aerobic exercise. Or have I exaggerated that because it's easier to find time to laugh than to exercise?

∾

Eleanor restored order again, and I straightened in my chair. "My dears, we've gone from being sad to being silly. Let's attack this subject with a bit more analysis. Loss.' The floor is open for discussion."

"Okay, I'll start," Ellen said. "I lost my husband several years ago, and I still can't get past the sensation that he'll come walking into the kitchen at any moment and ask what's for dinner. He was a wonderful man, I loved him and I concluded at the time, and I still believe, that life is not fair."

"The unfairness of life. That's easy to agree with. When I lost my husband, I truly felt as though the world had come to an end," Kelly said. "And in many ways it had. Did you feel that you had lost not only your husband but a whole way of life? I sure did. Suddenly the house was too big, the friends were too busy with 'couple' activities, the hours were too long, my interest in socializing too slight for me to bother. I eventually sold the house, moved into a neighborhood where there were more built-in activities and started all over again."

"That sounds terrifying to me," Susan protested. "I love my life, I love my house and I even love my husband! I can't imagine coping so well with such a loss."

"Can't imagine . . . I was about to say that imagining has nothing to do with it, but actually, imagination is *everything*. I found that I had to imagine a life for myself and then set about building it. Don't think this was some heroic act on my part. It was pure self-preservation," Kelly commented soberly.

"I never admitted this to anyone before," Rachel said, "and I don't want you to think I didn't love my husband, but I found some relief when he died. He had been sick for a long time. He had no quality of life left, and it hurt so much to see him listless and ill. It also drained me physically. Because we had been so close, he wanted me to be his sole caregiver, and I tried to do it well. I would have to say that the other side of my loss was liberation. I feel guilty saying that, but it's true."

"Well, if we insist on letting truth break out," Eleanor said, "let me say that I felt that my divorce, painful as it was, also became a liberation. I had structured my life to fit within his, and the fit was never right. Sort of like big feet in narrow shoes, that's how I saw myself. Now I only wear comfortable shoes that fit my feet. It's my own little joke."

"An important thing to consider here, and one I've thought about a lot, is that we are too often living someone else's agenda for our lives, instead of our own," said Susan. "It's another variation of our earlier discussions about the need to make *our own* choices – or at the very least, a compromise of mutual choices. No wonder you felt liberated."

Kelly mused, "Wouldn't you agree that, at least initially, it's usually *not* a feeling of liberation? It's devastation. Talking with other women,

I believe I can say with justification that it's hell! Your whole world is ripped away from you, most especially the best and closest friend you ever had, the love of your life, or at least for an important part of your life. For me, losing is not about liberation."

"Of course, you're right, if we're really being honest," Ellen answered. "I could scarcely breathe some days after my husband died. And I consider myself one of the lucky ones. Our home was paid off, our children were grown, I knew how to manage money and I had friends. I worry about women who still haven't gotten the message that loss is inevitable and you'd better know your financial picture sooner rather than later."

"Having a career or a significant volunteer job really helped me out," Laura said. "I had a world to which I belonged that was separate and apart from my husband's. Wonderful as it is to be your husband's best friend, you need other friends too, ones who can make you feel the world will go on somehow. As I'm thinking about it now, I admit that travel can become less attractive when you first lose a mate. I loved to travel, but my husband and I always went together, and I had a hard time getting started again on my own."

Rachel retorted, "Not for me it wasn't! I started traveling with teenage grandsons and found the experience wonderful. We established a closeness and created memories that we all still treasure. I felt cared for, and they felt valued – and lucky."

"I like that idea," Ellen said. "I'm picturing a cruise with just me and my grandchildren. What a bonding experience that could be. It could be a real treat for their parents, too!"

～

Free time? Oh, can I relate to that, I thought. I would just love to have a weekend free with my husband while my children were entertaining and being entertained by grandparents. I wondered if I could adopt this woman or if she would adopt me and my kids.

～

They talked for some time about funny incidents they encountered as women traveling alone or with other women and the lessons they learned. They started reciting them, as though the lessons were from a textbook:

- Demand a decent table in a restaurant; don't let them stick you in the back by the kitchen.

- Keep an open mind. You may find you like to travel alone. It's a great way to meet new and interesting people, or at least to avoid dull ones.

- Don't be afraid to eat alone; you may meet interesting people that way. Take a good book with you. Rachel noted that most married couples don't talk to each other in a restaurant anyway, so why be embarrassed if you're not talking to someone while you eat?

- Find a compatible traveling companion who likes the kinds of trips and arrangements that you like. You'll feel more comfortable with a friend, and you'll avoid those infernal charges for single passengers.

- Find a group to travel with, like the Smithsonian or Road Scholar, where others on the trip are interested in the same things.

- Take your grandchildren on trips. You'll form bonds with them and see sights in a totally different light.

- Look for bed-and-breakfast accommodations as a way of being in a comfortable setting. Always go to the hot tub.

$\sim$

That brought huge laughter from them, but I didn't get the joke. These ladies seemed a little more, shall we say, adventuresome than I would have first guessed.

⌒

- Find *Cheers* kind of places, familiar haunts where you can be comfortable and be yourself.

- However you do it, get out there. See the world.

"Okay, now that I've had my say about the devastation of losing someone you love," Kelly said, "I'm willing to agree there are aspects of loss that can be liberating. It's hard, though, don't you think?"

They all agreed.

"Think of it, you're suddenly single and you're reinventing yourself," Eleanor said. "At a stage in your life when you thought you knew yourself and your roles, you're abruptly in a different place. You begin to find out new things about yourself — what you like, what makes you happy. Suddenly, when all of the choices are yours, you're on a journey of discovery. You find your strength, wisdom, adaptability . . ."

"Your own personal agenda," Susan cheerfully interjected.

"I'd really like to take this topic up again from the standpoint of preparation for what may be inevitable," Eleanor said. "We have to consider the number of women who are likely to spend many years of their lives as single women, rather than as women with mates. We may be those very women. Let's talk next time about building a village for ourselves — with the keen realization that none of us is immune to loss. So let's remember the key points from today:

- Loss is inevitable.

- Be prepared. Know your resources. Don't be a victim.

- Life can seem fundamentally unfair at the moment of loss, and it is. But, don't forget, you have choices.

- Give yourself time and space. No one else can tell you when your grieving process should be complete.

- Recognize that loss has another side to it: liberation. Take advantage of the opportunity to get to know yourself again.

- Give yourself the freedom to decide what makes you happy, and act on it."

I'm so glad I didn't play hooky today. And I admit to being relieved that the weather is so lovely while I'm contemplating loss and grief. My wise women have handled these issues so well, and after their discussion, I'm reminded that I, too, will have to deal with them in my life—although I've been in blissful denial until now. Thanks to them, I now have some ideas about coping and surviving with courage.

And on a different note, as I'm coming down the home stretch on my thesis, and changing my focus toward a career combined with a family, I need to consider what really brings me joy. So much to think about!

Creating a Village.

Who will be here with me?

I wore casual clothes as usual, but I felt as though I should have dressed in a rumpled khaki raincoat and a slouch hat. I determined to be a spy and get a look at the women I'd been listening to for weeks.

I planned to slip down to the lobby before they finished today's discussion, lurk by the elevator and casually observe them as they leave. I've tried not to form an image of them before I actually lay eyes on them, but it's been hard.

~

Eleanor lost no time today getting the group settled in and ready to go, saying, "I'd like to remind y'all that last week we agreed on today's topic – one of my personal favorites – 'Creating a Village'. I've really been looking forward to it. Learning how to create my 'village' was an important milestone in my life, and it was helpful in my recovery from behaviors that weren't effective or healthy. I believe many women can benefit from it, and so I'd like to share the background and details now.

"After I was divorced, I really felt that I was out there in the cold world very much on my own. I wanted a man in my life. It was difficult for me to admit this because I was climbing the corporate ladder, daily rubbing elbows with women who were disinclined to think of themselves as being in any way dependent on men. Believe me, I tried reading all the books about how to live happily and alone, but it is still painful to recall how desperately lonely I felt much of the time.

"I tried to suppress my feelings, but when I still felt empty after cooking and eating gourmet food solo, I tried filling that emptiness with the quick fix of some man. You should have seen the ongoing series of dysfunctional men I allowed into my life! I couldn't have made these people up. Some of them were like characters right out of book by Carl Hiaasen. In retrospect, the experiences seem funny, but at the time they just added to my sense of tragedy that I was alone and I didn't want to be alone. Worst of all, I felt that there was something wrong with me that I craved companionship.

"So, it was a revelation to me when, in graduate school, I read a book by Dr. George Kelly. I can still picture the book in front of me. Kelly said that people are not designed to be independent. In fact, he emphasized that people have always grouped together for safety and emotional well being. So, we are all dependent. But, he warned not to put 'all one's eggs in one basket' – in other words, not to depend solely on one person. Kelly used the term 'interdependent' to describe a better way to have relationships. He might even have coined that term.

"It was a 'Eureka moment' for me. Interdependent! It was so simple, yet profound, that I could hardly believe I hadn't understood it before. Depending on one person had always left me at risk. I could be happy only if that person were treating me lovingly. And, of course, focusing on only one person meant that other people who could have been helpful and enjoyable were mostly out of the loop and, therefore, unavailable to me. The image of 'the village' came to me. In earlier times, we all lived in villages. We were interdependent. We had others nearby to count on. We had familiar, available and, hopefully, nurturing neighbors.

"Now when women come to therapy having lost a partner through death or divorce, I encourage them to create villages for themselves.

I think of these villages in physical terms along the lines of the little villages people sometimes construct under Christmas trees, along with train sets. In each village there are many structures, all of them a bit different from each other and serving different functions, but there is a unity to them. That unity comes from the *prime mover*, the person who chooses the pieces for the village and personally arranges them.

"As I've thought about this over time, I've realized that the person who creates the village can add to it or take pieces away or rearrange it, or even abandon it and create a whole new village in another space. For me this has been a powerful metaphor."

"Wow, that's a very strong image, a great metaphor, Eleanor. I especially like it," Kelly said, "because it allows for change. We've all realized that life is not static. Sometimes the friends you've cultivated for your village move away."

"Hey, maybe they secede from your village," Laura joked.

"Or a hut gets washed away by events," Kelly added. "I think about the huts that were in my village when I had kids in school. Once we didn't have kids in common any more, we lost that sense of interdependence. I found myself making new connections with people who were interested in the hobbies and volunteer work that I finally had time for."

"This village concept seems like a colorful way of saying that ya gotta have friends." Rachel broke into a bit of the old song. "Friendship is critical to a happy, healthy life. In fact, I've often thought that friends can do for us what family members may or may not be able to do. They are often better sounding boards and more empathetic about life's experiences and our reactions to them."

"Sometimes better even than spouses," added Ellen. "I always felt that my husband was my best friend, and I know that I was his best friend. Still, there were times when I needed a friend who was simply and purely a friend."

"Women seem better at that than men, don't you think?" Laura asked. "Get a group of women together, and in a short period of time they're sharing very personal information about life, love, setbacks and fears. Get a group of men together, and the conversation almost always involves sports teams and sports figures – people and events at a safe distance from their personal lives."

Susan added, "That might be stereotyping, but it probably is true more often than not. Still, I know many women who have become very isolated in their lives. It can happen insidiously when a woman is married and so busy with husband, children and obligations. Communication with friends sometimes diminishes until it disappears. Then, when she most needs a friend, there is no one to turn to."

"Yes, and we know that the most important rule of friendship is that if you want to *have* a friend, you must *be* a friend. There's a cost there – a cost of time and attention," Ellen said. "But it is time well spent. I can't imagine how women who have been isolated within their marriages deal with divorce or the death of their spouses. It would be as if their whole village were hit by a tsunami."

"I certainly felt that way," Ellen explained. "If I hadn't had friends as well as family and all those pieces of my village built from my professional life and community contacts, I might have fallen apart."

"You have a knack of making friends wherever you go," Susan responded. "Not everyone is like that. Not everyone can. Or maybe I should say that not everyone does. It takes effort, as you said."

"That's right. Maybe you can find villages that are already well-formed and you can move your hut right up close to the other huts. But I think we need to find relationships that fit our own special needs." Laura's tone got very serious as she continued. "I have to tell you about a part of my village that gives me a tremendous sense of comfort. Another woman and I made a pact that whenever either one of us has any serious medical issue, the other will come along as that person's eyes and ears. We realized in the process of taking care of our husbands that the persons being cared for are way too stressed to cope with everything that's happening and all the medical personnel who come and go. There needs to be a dedicated person near by who can remain objective and focused. So I guess I have a medical hut in my village."

"I can imagine taking this metaphor to the edge of silliness. Is your village infested with rats? With termites? Call us and we'll fumigate the place," Rachel quipped.

"Humorous as that is," Kelly said, "I can still relate to it. When

I started dating again, I found that what I thought of as my village was actually just one big hut. I felt really constrained in my relationships and activities. I was concerned that new friends and new pastimes would not be acceptable with my old crowd. I don't know whether you would say that I had to add more huts to my village or that I had to find a whole new village; but, in fact, I moved out of my old home and into a totally different kind of neighborhood. It was very freeing."

"Please assure me that no one brought craft materials and wants us to make little houses and label them as a concluding exercise." Laura seemed to be joking while still sounding serious. "I've been in too many groups where sophisticated ideas like this — being the architects of our own lives, choosing different friends for different needs, making and ending connections — were discussed and then the group dissolved into ticky-tacky craft projects. I don't do glue or scissors.

"All right, everyone, whoever brought the balsam wood and the paint sets, either confess or trash them immediately!"

Eleanor pushed through the good-natured jibes, and asked, "Can we pull our ideas together, though, as usual? We didn't say this explicitly as we discussed the concept of the village, but I think we have, in fact, addressed a question we wanted to answer: *Who will be with me as I age?* Our collective experience says that we can't count on spouses or companions to be with us forever. We hope that we can count on family, of course, especially children, if there are any. Very importantly, though, we have agreed that it is important for each of us to learn to create and maintain villages for ourselves, and to change them when they no longer suit our needs and preferences."

- Everyone needs a village of her own making.

- Villages are not static. They can and do change, sometimes because we want them to change and other times because change is inevitable.

- We are interdependent by virtue of being human. Celebrate that fact.

- We can't know in advance who will be with us at any point

in our lives. Keep refreshing the village, and be willing to maintain your presence in the villages of others.

~

At that point, taking advantage of their usual last-minute exchanges, I exited my 'spot' and headed quickly down the stairs. I found a hiding place behind a convenient tall display of books. If any of my friends had seen me, seemingly engrossed in books for young kids about race cars and race drivers, they would have been astonished. I'm always the one in the slow lane — even on the highway. This display of books, however, provided me perfect cover for my purpose.

Despite my best efforts, I had time for only a brief glimpse. But, it wasn't just that I didn't have enough time; my emotional response was the real obstacle to the identification process. My first — unexpected — impression was: 'Oh, my gosh! They look just like the girls next door, only grown up.' Eavesdropping on them, listening to their stories, I'd created larger-than-life figures. There were women who resembled family members, neighbors and friends. Just regular folks.

What was obvious, however, even in my brief observation, was that my impression of their interactions was right on target. As they walked through the lobby and out the doors, their interactions were easy, lively and frequently punctuated with laughter.

I looked forward to next week, when I returned to my spot and listened in on them once again.

When You Have
All the Time in the World,
What Do You Have Time for?

Remaining relevant and solvent

For all their outbursts of hilarity, I think of my women as having "gravitas." They seem rooted in who they are and how they approach life. I've never been fond of the saying, "Bloom where you are planted," because I have lived in several parts of the country, had a couple of different career paths, and I like to think I'm imaginative enough to pull up roots and make a successful move elsewhere if necessary. These women, however, gave me a different perspective on the slogan. It's not so much about being rooted in a place as being rooted in oneself. That philosophy I like very much.

Today, though, for all that gravitas, they sound "all atwitter," like a gaggle of girls instead of an assembly of wise women. Oh, someone has a boyfriend!

～

"How long has this been going on?"

"What's he like?"

"Is he treating you well?"

"Come on, we want all the news. Look, she's blushing."

∾

"She" turned out to be Laura.

∾

"Now, it's just a friendship," Laura tried to say. But, the group was having none of it.

"Oh, no, that's not what I heard," Ellen said. "Details, please."

"Well, really, it is a friendship. At least it had been that way for several years. We have started dating, though . . ."

"I knew it; I knew it. It's the quiet ones you've got to watch."

"And, so, *now*? You're dating and so . . ."

"Well, he's a bit younger than I am. Quite a bit younger."

"Laura's a cougar!" someone called out.

"A cougar?" That stopped them in their tracks. "What's a cougar?"

"Don't you know? A cougar is an older woman who has what it takes to attract the young guys. That's our Laura!"

"Now I really am embarrassed," Laura protested. "I'm an older widow who happens to have a very close relationship with a man who happens to be younger."

"Hmmm. Lots of 'happen-ings' in there, Laura," Rachel said. "So what exactly *is* happening?"

"Eleanor, isn't it time to change the subject?" Laura pleaded.

"Far be it from me to take you off center stage, Laura," Eleanor said. "I want to know all about him, too, and, of course, we just want the best for you."

"And we want all the savory details, too," Ellen added.

"For now, though, we'll let our little cougar off the hook." Eleanor interjected. "Still, it certainly relates to our intended topic today – that of remaining relevant and solvent. We might take Laura's new romance as an example of remaining relevant . . ."

Laura squeaked.

". . . then acknowledge that at every stage in life, new and unexplored paths can open up, if we're prepared to change and explore."

"Sometimes, of course, those paths open up and you feel as though you've been hit by a two-by-four. Not, of course, that I think that's true in your case, Laura," Susan teased.

~

I could hear Laura groaning while the others laughed. *They still have a touch of teenager in them, especially today*, I thought.

~

"More often, though," Eleanor continued, "I think we fear nothing new and unique will happen as we age, for good or for ill. It's easy to settle into accustomed patterns and literally bore ourselves to death. I'm sorry to say that I've seen this happen to some older women. Personally, I have more new things I want to explore than I have time for, so it surprises me when I see people settle for a tedious lifestyle and think it's a reasonable way to live."

Ellen advised, "A physician friend once told me that there are three things you have to do every day to remain a vibrant human being: exercise, do something for someone else and create something with lasting power — such as a craft project, a painting, a letter, a song or a garden — the idea being to create something tangible that you can see or hear. He was certain that doing nothing was a direct path to illness."

"I love that, especially the second one," Kelly said. "We can enrich our own lives by enriching others. I've encountered people who feel that they've given enough over a lifetime, whether it's treasure or talent or time, and they feel they have earned the right to sit back and avoid participation. That seems so sad and so misguided to me. When I give something — especially time — to help on a project or charity, or help someone else have a better day, I feel younger. There may even be a mathematical equation to it: Energy expended on good deeds equals energy gained to the tenth power."

"You feel that way, Kelly," said Rachel, "Because you recognize better than many that real fulfillment comes from helping others."

"You're reminding me of an aunt of mine," Laura said, "who felt so sorry for herself when her husband died that she took to her chair and her books and surfaced at family gatherings only long enough to bemoan the fact that she had nothing to do."

"Nothing to do and all the time in the world to do it in," Ellen sighed. "Now that would be my description of sheer hell. I can't even imagine it."

"Of course you can't, because you were never that way," Susan said." I strongly believe that the older we get, the more like our basic selves we become. Interesting people become even more interesting. Responsible, kind, generous people become more so. Those who appear to become narcissistic with age were really that way all along, and, when they were younger, they were able to conceal those traits. There could probably be a mathematical equation for that, too!"

"Consensus on this topic is going to be amazingly easy. Considering the lives you've led, the people you are today, the difficulty in finding free time for our meetings, and then, the difficulty in ending the sessions once you've engaged on a topic, I'd say we all believe in remaining relevant, active and involved. Perhaps staying relevant does come naturally to certain personality types or women who have already had certain experiences. What, though, could we recommend to someone like Laura's aunt with her chair and her books and her boredom?" Eleanor asked.

"We should make a list," Kelly said with excitement. "If we put our thoughts together, I'm sure we could come up with enough ideas of all sorts to fill at least a hundred lifetimes. We could start with volunteer activities that are really fun — not the kinds where your assignment is to sit in a room and stuff envelopes."

"Right," Susan agreed, "because many people in our modern age, with its youth-oriented culture, think of aging in terms of diminishment. They find it easy to dismiss those of us who have passed a certain age. I prefer Margaret Mead's attitude. She believed that women about the age of fifty, having finished the nesting phase of their lives, are poised to do some of their best work. Think of the amount of money the people around this table have raised for worthy causes, the number of young people that we've mentored, and the political clout we've wielded. We're able to do more than ever."

"I agree. Let's devote a section in our list to the fantastic volunteer opportunities here and even in other countries, since we're at an age where we can travel and not inconvenience a family." Rachel added. "Let's be sure to add educational opportunities, too, such as seminars and classes. I've enjoyed the Road Scholar program several times. Or 'Hostile Elders,' as I heard one particularly disgruntled professor call it once. He was obviously a person who was old and crabby before his time."

"Let's add a section on the marvelous new ways we have to stay connected." Kelly said. "Keeping in touch with friends and family through e-mail and Facebook is wonderful. Technology is really a gift to us as we age – if we can just get past the fear of pushing the wrong button."

"Yes," added Susan. "I'm glad you're mentioning the importance of connections, because we need to remember that relationships can't flourish – even within friends and family – without communication."

"And there's a whole new vocabulary – Twittering, Tweets – I can hardly keep up," Ellen said.

"That's why we have grandchildren. They have the patience to teach us."

"Can we acknowledge, though, that while it can be intoxicating to have so many possibilities open to us as we age, it can also be scary?" Laura asked. "As we've said before, when you're told that suddenly you can do anything you want to do, there's a paralysis that can set in. *Anything?* That's intimidating."

"Nevertheless, don't you think that happiness at any age, and maybe more so as we age, is bound up in striving?" asked Susan. "If we open our eyes and look about us, an interesting goal will show itself soon enough."

"Granted," Ellen said. "Let's not create a stereotype in which every senior citizen has to rush out and sign up for computer classes and a trip to the Galapagos to care for sea turtles. The point is to be true to yourself. If you want to be the best self you can be, you need to select pursuits that give you energy and enthusiasm."

"Yes, back to our three daily activities: exercise, do something for someone else, create something with lasting power."

"How about the solvency aspect, Eleanor? You mentioned that along with relevancy. Relevancy seems like a much happier topic." Laura said.

"It's certainly a happier topic if there is *already* solvency. Older women need to realize, though, as they look at available opportunities, that remaining solvent is one of their obligations, at least in so far as it is under their control. It's no longer socially acceptable for a woman to act as though her financial position is too complicated for her to understand or too unladylike for her to master. A woman must know what money she has, how she has it invested and how much is available for her to live on. She may need to scale back on her living costs in light of that knowledge. In any case, she is the responsible party and needs to act that way."

"That's a bit harsher than any advice I've heard you give, Eleanor," Kelly said. "It must come from some encounters that prove that women can still be foolish about money."

"Yes, I've seen that in different ways. Some women become so paralyzed at the idea of handling their own affairs that they scale back to the point of being miserly with themselves, their family and their community. That's not advisable any more than it's advisable to spend beyond one's needs. Realism is critically important, based on good advice. A woman needs advice from someone she trusts who can review her assets and help her structure a plan."

"We can become the prey of the unscrupulous so easily, can't we?" Rachel added. "It breaks my heart when I hear of older people losing everything they worked for to a scam artist. Besides saying that a woman should find someone she can trust, are there more specific guidelines that you recommend?"

"I'll toss one in," said Susan. "In addition to getting appropriate advice, a woman needs to understand her financial information herself. She shouldn't just turn everything over to someone and then assume all will be well — no matter the credentials of that trusted someone. If her previous financial affairs were completely handled by others, then she needs to start from scratch — and it's so much easier than she might think. A simple listing of all her assets minus all her liabilities, for example, will produce her net worth. If the woman is computer literate enough to e-mail, she can add easy-to-use software to her computer that will categorize her income and outgo with ease. My son put the program in my computer many years ago, and by just using my checkbook to type into the program, my accounting needs immediately became simplicity itself! Of course, a woman will probably benefit from a trusted C.P.A. or attorney who can keep her abreast of current investments or tax law changes."

"I think those are excellent comments, Susan," said Eleanor. "A Certified Public Accountant can guide you through financial and investment decisions of all kinds to maximize future financial resources."

Ellen added. "It's important to avoid putting a family member in the difficult position of being the person you rely on as your financial guru. All too often, I've seen terrible strains on family relationships that result. I recommend a safe distance from all relatives when it comes to finances just to keep everything objective and to avoid stirring up real or imagined tensions."

"Objectivity is important. There must be sound financial knowledge and an understanding about the woman's goals," Susan said. "An advisor who wants me to think like a forty-year-old when it comes to investing and spending would cause me great angst. I can rarely again add appreciably to my assets. I can't afford to take a lot of chances. 'Slow and steady wins the game' might be the best motto."

"I never put myself in the position of telling my clients how to handle their finances or who would be the best person to handle them. That's very risky and it would require that I know a lot more about their financial situation than I need to know." Eleanor advised. "I recommend, though, that if they don't have a financial advisor, they consider getting one. There's nothing charming about poverty as one gets older; and there's nothing charming about miserliness and financial paralysis."

"We've covered some tough subjects," added Eleanor. "Let's go from there into a summary of today's session —

- Remaining relevant is essential to remaining well and happy.

- A good plan for a day that is relevant and adds more energy than it takes is:

  Exercise
  Do something for someone else
  Create something with lasting power

- There are multiple opportunities to make life more meaningful and enjoyable at any age. Pick one, pick two, or pick many! Choose and act on your choices.

- Technology is more of a value than a threat. Enter the internet age and see all it offers you.

- Remaining solvent is important to anyone who wishes to remain relevant and happy. Understand that you are responsible for your financial position and seek advice to maximize it.

- To update Ben Franklin: neither a miser nor an irresponsible spender be.

Putting money away for retirement! We can barely meet our bills, with my school expenses and the kids growing faster than I can shop. But I think what The Pages have taught me today is that it is not too early to plan, even if I can't carry out my plans immediately. I've noticed free seminars offered by investment specialists in the community, and I could begin that education pretty painlessly right now.

It's Not All Snow and Mistletoe:
Holidays and Families — or Not.

Relating to grown children and grandchildren

Assertiveness has never been my strong point. In fact, a friend of mine once gave me a book on becoming more assertive and eventually demanded it back. He said I was a hopeless case.

So I astonished even myself when I arrived at the library and found someone else occupying my accustomed place. I debated with myself a bit about whether to disturb this interloper, realizing that, of course, I had no claim to the spot. Today, however, was my day for working on my dissertation, as well as my special time for eavesdropping on my women. For my eavesdropping, no other place would do.

I accosted her nicely, of course, and she looked at me as though I were quite mad. Frankly, I felt a bit mad and not very articulate. How could I fully explain how important a group of perfect strangers had become to me, and how essential it was to continue eavesdropping? I muttered on for a while about the light, my usual spot, the strength of the wireless signal, the value of having the same work set-up every time. Finally, she seemed to simply give up in the face of my incessant ramblings, glanced at me one last time as though I shouldn't be allowed out by myself, and walked away. I probably gave her an amusing incident to relate to her friends and family — the half-mad writer who needed a certain spot in the library for heaven-knows-what-reason.

I knew the reason. I wanted to know what they were going to talk about this week. By the time I settled in, the women had already begun in earnest.

～

"I've come to hate holidays, really," Ellen was saying. "I used to love them — decorating the house, preparing special foods, everyone together. Now my favorite holiday is Columbus Day. No one expects anything special on Columbus Day."

In a consoling voice, Kelly asked, "Can't you simply tell your family you don't want to do all that holiday stuff any more and get them to share the load? When I delegate the responsibilities among the family, I have time to enjoy the celebration along with them."

"For me, though, that's not the issue," Ellen responded. "Each of them wants to celebrate the holiday in their own home, and they each invite me."

"That's an issue? I'd say that's a triumph! I'd love to feel so wanted."

Ellen was not to be dissuaded. "No, no, it *is* an issue, at least until cloning becomes commonplace and I can split my cloned selves into different parts of the country simultaneously. Two of the children are mine and one is his. No matter where I go, the other two are irritated, especially now that my husband is gone. It becomes a matter of family loyalty."

Laura tried another approach. "Have you tried dividing up the holidays and setting out a long-range plan? In this particular year, you agree to go to one house for Thanksgiving and the other house for Christmas and someone else's house for the Fourth of July. And the next year, you switch the order."

"And if it's Memorial Day, and you're in Belgium, you must have spilled coffee on the master calendar," Rachel added, with laughter.

"So everyone gets a chance to have you visit for an important holiday," Susan commented. "I still think you're lucky beyond belief that all of them want you. In some families, the surviving spouse isn't so sought after — they're only invited out of obligation."

"Oh, I'm sounding ungrateful, aren't I? I don't mean to be; I love them all. I just hate being in a position where I feel as if I'm walking on eggshells every time a holiday comes along. Aren't holidays supposed to be fun?"

Kelly seemed to be wondering out loud when she spoke, "While I personally still love to have my entire family come to my home, that doesn't have to be your preference. Have you asked yourself what *you* most want to do for the holidays?"

"That's *it*, Kelly. That's the question to ask!" Susan prompted with excitement. "What would *you* really like to do? This must be a fairly common dilemma."

Rachel added, "I have friends who've told me they spent holidays looking at their watches, or counting the days until they could return home to their comfort zones. Of course, they appreciated being invited to their children's homes, and they seemed to be in a no-win situation: ungrateful if they weren't enjoying themselves or ungrateful if they chose to stay home."

"That's confusing for me," said Laura. "I'd prefer to avoid labeling my preferences as 'ingratitude' just because my choices aren't the same as someone else's. Time is passing. If we can't spend holidays in ways that make us happy, what are we thinking? Last year I decided to do something I've always wanted to do — spend Christmas in Germany. A friend of mine and I signed up for a cruise through the Christmas markets along the Rhine, and we loved every minute of it. I missed being with the family, but they had a wonderful holiday based on their choices, and so did I. None of us had any regrets when it was all over."

"I guess I'm more like Kelly," Susan commented. "I would not want to be away from my family at Christmas or Thanksgiving."

"Well, don't be," said Laura, "and, by the way, there are many ways to celebrate holidays — other than the traditional ones. One summer, my family decided to celebrate everyone's birthday at one time. It was perfect. We rented this wonderful, big beach house. We all traveled just once; we saw each other in a setting that belonged to no single one of us; and we all shared in the cooking and clean-up. And, best of all, just before anyone got on each other's nerves — or any old grievances could break through — the week was over, and we all went home happy."

Kelly sounded pleased and promptly agreed. "Thanks, Laura. That sounds like a great idea. Have you ever seen those cruises where you take the whole family, children included, out to sea for a week? That looks like such fun to me, and it's another way to get everyone together so that Grandma doesn't have to choose among the grandchildren. She can be with all of them!"

"Isn't it interesting how different we all are, even with respect to our ideas about holidays? Many of my friends prefer smaller groups and find ways to visit one set of relatives at a time," Ellen countered. "And what about solo holidays? Sometimes, they just crave a quiet getaway. Have any of you spent holidays away from the usual places?"

"I think B&Bs are ideal for those kinds of holidays," Rachel replied. "We've talked about them before as good solutions for women traveling alone. They are often beautifully decorated for the season. You can have a 'dose' of people for a while, and then you can retreat to a book, or take a walk, or do whatever you want to do — yet you are not completely alone as you'd be in a hotel room."

Eleanor chimed in at this point saying, "I'm pleased that we've generated so many attractive sounding options for holidays, but I'm aware that presenting these changes to families, who are used to status-quo, isn't always easy. Some of my clients say it's been difficult for them to tell their sons or daughters that they prefer staying close to home during a holiday. However, their decisions seem to gain more acceptance when they say they have specific plans, and in particular, plans that include being with neighbors or friends.

"And, talking about joining friends reminds me," she continued. "Remember our conversation about creating your own 'village' — your network for social support? Holidays are often difficult for my clients who don't have families, or at least families nearby. I encourage them to take these opportunities to reach out to others who are alone — to invite friends and neighbors to their homes for 'covered dish' gatherings. If we look around, there are usually people who would appreciate being included."

"Or maybe they would prefer not to travel and be at big family gatherings and they'd really enjoy just going down the street," added Ellen.

"Now, I wonder," asked Eleanor, "if we can leave the topic of holidays with or without families and move on to a larger subject — everyday relationships with grown children, step-children and grandchildren. Do you feel ready to plunge into that difficult water?"

"Difficult, indeed," Kelly said. "To continue that water metaphor, I felt at times while raising my children as though I were swimming in Jell-O. Some periods of our lives together seemed so hard. Relating to them now that they are adults, though, brings a new set of issues — or at least it can."

"One of my proudest moments as a mother was when my daughter and her husband bought a house that I definitely did not approve of," Rachel said, "and I didn't say a single negative word. I kept reminding myself that they didn't need my opinion and that it wasn't my house. Obvious as that sounds, I think it's a knotty situation when your impulse is to continue treating your children as if they were still young, when they want to be treated as adults."

"I agree with you, Rachel," Kelly said. "It's even harder where the grandchildren are concerned. Although I laugh when I hear my son sounding like his father, there are other moments when I so want to intervene and tell the grand kids how to behave. But, of course, unless I'm babysitting, I need to step back and let them handle it their way."

"Oh! That reminds me," Ellen added with intensity. "When I saw what my granddaughter was wearing to school one day, I almost bit my tongue off, trying to keep the words in my mouth. And, of course, I wanted to say something to my daughter-in-law. But I'm sure that wouldn't have been good for our relationship. I have opinions, based on years of experience; I can see possible pitfalls; and, I want so much to express my opinions. But I don't. It's really not my place to do this."

~

Well, I agreed, too! They'd think it was really odd to hear someone talking to them through the library wall, but I was so tempted to add my opinion to the discussion. I couldn't imagine the chaos at my house if our kids got one set of instructions from us and another set from his parents and another from my parents. The children would be confused, and I would be really irritated.

~

Eleanor said, "The stories of how parents don't get along with grown children and step-children are, unfortunately, legion. They make very funny or very depressing movies. Let's talk, though, about ways to make those relationships work effectively. What has worked for y'all?"

Rachel responded, speaking thoughtfully, "I believe in saying what I think. If they don't like it, I'm sure they can deal with it."

Kelly quietly disagreed, "It seems to me that the frank approach you're suggesting, Rachel, might work with what color to paint a room, or even issues like politics or religion, but I couldn't be blunt with my children when it came to personal issues. My rule is simple: keep it to yourself. The harmony in the relationship is more important than what I think, even if I'm right."

"Harmony. Yes. And respect! I like those concepts." Susan said the words as though they were the most beautiful in the world. "Pay less attention to whether we approve of their lifestyles or their decisions and more attention to the preservation of harmony and mutual respect. The world our children live in is so different from the world we've experienced, just as ours was from the world of our parents'. I try to remember that, even though I think of myself as reasonably intelligent, I can be mistaken, especially in these interesting times."

"Now there's wisdom: the willingness to admit that you're wrong! You may doubt that I have that ability, but really, I do. It's just that I don't need to very often," chuckled Rachel.

"Wait, wait," Eleanor said earnestly. "Since we began by discussing strategies we use to respect our families' choices, I assume we are still talking about how we handle our feelings and opinions when we disagree with theirs. I want to be sure we're not saying that we should stuff our feelings and opinions all the time. It was beginning to sound like we were advocating 'peace at any price', and I spend many therapy hours teaching and encouraging women to be assertive."

"I think you've already heard my response on that one," said Rachel with good-humored laughter.

"And mine," said Susan. "That harmony cannot truly exist without mutual respect."

Ellen said, "Perhaps we can borrow something from previous discussions. I think our ways of coping should differ depending on whose 'turf' we're talking about. If it's my turf and my decisions to make, then my highest priority is to make choices that enhance my life. I am less concerned about harmony, then, although I'd always prefer that my family felt good about our interactions. When it comes to my children's turf, then my highest priorities are respect and harmony."

~

That sounded familiar. I recalled making myself a note from one of their earlier meetings, something like, "You gotta know when to hold and when to fold." I was glad I didn't miss this session. I had just assumed that my parents wanted us to come to their house for the holidays, and I'd even been a bit resentful because I wanted to establish some traditions in my own home. And when we'd had other disagreements, I sometimes fell back into acting like a child instead of acting like an adult. An adult would have a conversation with her parents about conflicts. I might find out that, like some of these women, they'd like to change things around a bit, too. And I have added respect now for my parents and in-laws, because they have never, ever treated my husband and me as anything but adults — other than spoiling the children, and the kids of course love that — they haven't tried to usurp our authority.

Oops, while I was reflecting, they moved on to the topic of grandchildren.

~

"Do you remember that vintage movie with Ernest Borgnine in which his mother shuffles around in an old sweater and slippers, and he remarks about her being fifty? How times have changed," Ellen said. "Now the grandmothers I know are more like us — out and about, some still working full-time, others busy with volunteer activities and hobbies and travel."

" 'Oh, my sainted grandmother.' Did you ever hear that phrase? Was there a time when grandmothers were saintly?" Kelly asked.

"Yes, when they died young. A consequence of our living longer takes away some of that saintliness. Instead, we're as likely to get ourselves in trouble as our grandchildren are," said Rachel.

Laura countered: "That changes our relationship with them, doesn't it? The fact that we don't look or act as old could make them think we lack wisdom."

"I really dislike that joke about why grandparents and grandchildren get along so well," Rachel said. "The punch line is, 'Because they have a common enemy in the parents.' Actually, what we provide our grandchildren, that their parents often cannot, is time — the time to listen, with the added benefit that we don't have total responsibility for them."

"Being a grandparent is just the best job in the world," someone exclaimed!

"Right on!"

"You have that right!"

"We may be sounding a little like Pollyanna about this grandchildren gig," Ellen cautioned. "A neighbor of mine popped in for a respite from her precious grand kids. She said the television was on constantly, and she wondered if they could live without a remote control. And, she complained that when they weren't watching television, or on their cell phones or computers, they were so engrossed in video games and iPods that she doubted a fire alarm would have gotten their attention."

"As Susan said earlier, things now are very different than they were when we were raising our children," Rachel added. "I'm different, too. Noise, especially continual noise, unnerves me. And I hate video games. My grandson tried to get me to play a *Star Wars* video game with him, and I tried because I love spending time with him. Finally, though, he told me that he dropped me out of the game. He said I kept getting killed or starting a fight and I didn't know what I was doing. He was right."

"It seems only fair to set parameters in our own homes," said Laura. "As you mentioned earlier, Eleanor, that is my 'turf.' For example, in my house, kids dashing across the room and landing in the middle of the sofa is not acceptable. But I also try to be flexible when it comes to things like video games. I know they enjoy them, and as long as the sound is at a reasonable level, I let it go at that."

"Before we conclude," Eleanor added, "I'd like to emphasize again the importance of balance and creative choices. For example, when possible, visits with grandchildren can be planned in ways that are mutually pleasant and comfortable for both the children and the grandparents. It's up to *us* to set limits that work for us. As experienced women, we can hopefully assess situations and devise activities and plans that work for everyone's enjoyment, including our own."

"Right," echoed Ellen. "That reminds me of a wonderful story. My grandson loves baseball. Since I wanted to spend quality time with him, I went out in the yard and tried to play catch with him. The long and short of this tale is that neither of us were having fun! Rather than giving up the special time with him, I suggested that I teach him something that I enjoy – playing poker – and he loved it."

"I wonder what helped make you so good at it?" Susan asked with comradely humor.

"Yes, Susan, I'm grateful for the skills I learned around your table," laughed Ellen. "And what makes it even better is that now, as soon as I arrive at his home for a visit, he wants to know when we'll be able to play a few hands."

"Cool!" replied Susan.

Kelly said, "I've loved our discussion today, but I fear I'm about to be permanently adhered to this chair. Let's wrap it up and make our summary list. Here goes:

- Relationships with children and grandchildren work best when built on mutual respect.

- Treat your grown children as adults and act like an adult yourself. Talk with your children. Express your own wishes. Don't take for granted that they know what you want.

- Acting in your own self-interest is not necessarily selfish. And it's certainly better than feeling resentful when you simply go along.

- As a grandparent, you don't have the responsibilities for the grandchildren that their parents have. You don't have the rights, either, that go with parental responsibility. You do have the right to set reasonable boundaries in your own home.
- Silence is often the best response in preserving relationships, especially when it is about a choice that belongs on their "turf."

- Holidays are supposed to be fun. Figure out how to make them that way for your sake and for theirs.

∾

The meeting was especially informative for me. I'm glad that I was assertive (well, in a wimpy sort of way). They gave me a lot to think about in terms of how I relate with my parents and in-laws. We all get along well — in harmony — and seem to respect each other's "turf", to use two of today's terms, but I must admit that I hadn't thought about the factors that made our relationships work so well before today.

Am I Moving In — Or Out?
Is He? Or Are They?

New living situations

"I've seen the future and I'm not going there."

Kelly began talking while the women were getting seated, even before the usual chit-chat back and forth as The Pages caught up on their busy activities since the last meeting.

Laura sounded breathless after dashing in from one of her many volunteer activities, and Ellen apologized that she hadn't had time to change from her tennis shorts to more suitable clothing.

What active people! I thought.

"Well, that takes care of that," Rachel said. "Make a note that Kelly is not going to the future."

The others all laughed, but Kelly seemed quite serious.

"Goodness, Kelly," Ellen said. "What brought this on? You make it sound like this is more than just a passing notion."

"I got an invitation," Kelly said, "to an Open House at a retirement facility of some sort, the Pines of Lake Pembroke. What a name! Usually I throw things like that right into the recycling bin, but my neighbor really wanted to see what it was like, so we went."

"Retirement facilities have become quite varied these days," said Susan. "They can be straightforward facilities for independent living, or assisted living, or nursing care facilities – or my favorite total-complex facility, CCRCs. Which kind were you invited to?

"I think she said it was a continuing care retirement community", said Kelly.

"That's great, Kelly. That's a CCRC. These communities have reinvented many aspects of the old-fashioned concepts of retirement living over the past couple of decades," said Susan. "I hope you weren't disappointed."

"No," said Kelly. "Actually, it was quite lovely. It wasn't how it *looked* that spooked me. It was the idea that at some point I might have to give up my home, my sanctuary, my place of total independence, and live in some little rooms near a whole lot of old people. I'd have to learn to talk about bunions and rheumatism. All the live-long day, bunions and rheumatism."

The whole group laughed again, except for Kelly.

"You wouldn't be doing that, anyway," chuckled Ellen. "With your artistic eye and gentle ways, Kelly, you'd be spending your days painting portraits of all those rheumatic folk, and cheering them up, besides."

"Wait a minute, though" said Susan. "CCRCs aren't anything like Kelly's fears.

They often have large campuses with beautiful grounds that could comprise anything from a dozen acres to hundreds of acres, certainly enough land to offer extensive amenities on site, besides the usual meandering paths for walking and talking. And they're often in or near cities for easy mobility and cultural activities," Susan added. "I'm pretty enthusiastic about them."

But Kelly's aesthetic nature was evident as she responded, "I don't like the idea of institutional-looking buildings."

"Who does?" answered Susan. "I've visited friends and relatives in several CCRCs. I've seen residential units that vary from individual villas, duplexes, low-rises, mid-rises, high-rises or any mix thereof. However, I think the important thing to consider is that I'd expect the majority of one's years spent on these campuses would be times of reasonably good health, shared with existing and new friends. And, if they are needed at any point, there are facilities right there on campus where residents can receive whatever level of care is needed, not far from all their friends."

"You know," said Eleanor, "this is a very important topic for us to discuss. Let's take Kelly's concerns and explore them in some depth. Where we live is vitally important to who we are, how we perceive ourselves, and what options we see for ourselves."

Eleanor, who attended many seminars on aging, continued, "Recent studies suggest that declines associated with age are not as predictable or universal as was formerly believed, and that the degree of good health or impairment of health often depends on individual choices, patterns and environments."

Ellen asked the group, "So, is our topic for today 'New Living Situations'?"

Laura quickly responded, "I, frankly, am not interested in 'new' living situations. I've lived in my own home for a long time, and I like the feeling that my surroundings are a reflection of me. I like things the way I like them. Even though I'd formerly lived in a few different houses in different states, the house I live in today was always mine to do with as I pleased."

"I share some of that feeling," said Ellen. "But it doesn't always work out that way. When my husband died, I vowed I wouldn't leave my house voluntarily. I swore that someone would have to come and hogtie me and carry me away. How could I live without my favorite chair in the perfect corner for it, and the décor just right? Gradually, though, I didn't like what was happening to me in that house. Every little noise made me think, *Uh oh, a pipe is going to burst, the air conditioning unit is going to blow up, and termites have my house slated for their next feast.* Finally, I put the house on the market, bought a small condo with a management company that looks after things and gave myself piece of mind."

"That's fine *if* you can find another place that suits you," Laura said. "Right now, however, I can't imagine being anywhere else."

"Imagination," said Eleanor. "That's very important. We can't imagine lots of the things that actually happen to us. Wouldn't we be better prepared to have control over our own lives if we imagine some scenarios and how we'd like to handle them, if they occur?"

"I think that's good advice," said Kelly, "even though I don't like it. We're intelligent women; we've seen a lot; we've lived through a lot; we know that sometimes life comes at people like a tsunami and there's little time to think before acting. I do know that I don't want to be placed in a nursing home against my will — at a time when I might not be strong enough to protest. And I realize I might genuinely need someone to take care of me."

"I'm not in the least bit interested in someone taking care of me," said Rachel. "I hear people worry about whether their kids will offer to take care of them in later life. Well, I have news for my children. I do not want to live in their houses; I do not want them taking care of me. Nothing personal against them, but I just don't want that."

"Rachel," said Susan, "I would guess everyone in this room probably agrees with you. Society and longevity have changed the equations of living."

"You know, we might be the first civilization not to take care of our elders within the family unit," Susan said. "Even in Japan, women are fast disappearing from the home as they go into the workforce. And we know what that means. If there is not a woman in the home, there is unlikely to be a caregiver unless it's the husband caring for a wife. And even that's not for sure."

"Do you think that's a by product of Social Security?" Laura asked. "Before Social Security was enacted in 1935, an older person didn't have many options, so the family was the only solution, whether it wanted to be, or not. And even though Social Security had been intended as only a supplement to people's retirement income, rather than being counted on as their total income, the cost of living adjustments that were added in 1975 have helped retirees a lot."

"You know what's funny?" laughed Susan with delight at her own thought, "I just read in a lead story by a magazine's financial journalist that retirees should have a good nest egg to supplement their Social

Security. There's sure a turnabout in how we — and the 'financial experts' — now think of our retirement needs."

"Yes, it is," Laura agreed. "Anyway, now older people have more choices. Once upon a time, they might have been limited to moving in with their families when spouses died or they were no longer able to function independently."

"I heard a lecture recently on the myth of the nuclear family," Rachel said. "The researcher said that, in fact, we all want to believe that once there was a nuclear family that took care of the elderly. If we look back with care, however, we find that it was not the norm that a home had an elderly parent or relative living with a younger family."

"Probably because older people died off before they outlived their comfort zones," Laura quipped. "Now we get enough medication so that we live longer. We just can't necessarily live longer *comfortably*."

"Also, consider what it would be like to live in one of our children's homes these days," Ellen added. "Who would actually be home? Maybe the cat or dog. But mom and dad are working, the kids are at school, everyone rushes to soccer or dance class or 'play dates' on the weekend or after school. I stayed with my children once for a week. I never had so much time spent in solitude."

"So if we look at the idea that an older woman has options, but that those options may be constrained by her health or her family's situation . . ." Eleanor began.

"Or her finances . . ." one of them chimed in.

"Yes, let's definitely remember that finances play a big role in what options are open. All that being said — what, in fact, *is* being said?" Eleanor asked.

"I think we're saying that it's important to *consider* different living options and evaluate how suitable they are to us, individually. And to do it now, while we are not being forced to act on our options," Susan said.

From Laura: "Sort of 'think about this today' instead of 'think about this tomorrow'?"

And from Rachel: "Precisely."

She continued, "I'm still thinking about how women's lives might be compromised if they moved in with their children after serious health challenges, or life changes, such as being widowed. So much of my own sense of self has to do with 'attitude.' Would these women have the courage to re-build their lives once they were changed so drastically, or would they resign themselves to sitting back and letting their children's lifestyles dictate what they would or would not do? I cannot imagine pretending excitement over dinner with the family at McDonald's when my former self would have gotten dressed up, gone with friends to a restaurant with gourmet food, and shared a lovely bottle of wine."

"Let's not disparage the family as an option," Kelly said. "I might really like living with my children if there could be a certain part of the house that was designated as 'the grandmother's' quarters."

"Have you ever talked with your children about that?" Eleanor asked. "We may be presuming that certain accommodations can or can't be made, without actually checking it out."

"You're right, Eleanor," Ellen said. "I've been writing down 'Options' while we've been talking. Living with family is one of them, but if I think that through and leave it on my list, I should talk with my children about how they feel and whether there would be a way to arrange things so that they and I would be comfortable."

"Listening to you, Ellen, and to Laura," said Susan, "I'm reminded of some research showing positive results from living in a society or environment of some complexity, where one utilizes personal choice and cognitive abilities. The study said that these elements really enhance the vitality of aging – and longevity as well. Maybe we should be asking if living with one's children offers the complexity we might need and desire."

"That continuing care retirement community is beginning to look better to me," Kelly said. "I've just added it to my list of options, in spite of what I said before. I can see that I could still have a certain amount of privacy and independence, which I might lose if I chose the option of moving in with family."

"I've always said that before I would go into a retirement institution, I would throw myself in front of a very large truck." said Rachel. "But perhaps that does have to be on the list of options. Remember that joke about being nice to your children because they're the ones who will choose your nursing home? Well, this discussion has made me think that I should explore the different retirement communities in this area, what they're like, what they offer — just in case, you know. I still reject the idea outright. But if it became necessary, I'd feel better if I were the one who chose 'my possibly last home', if I were the one who set the criteria."

"Very smart," Eleanor said. "It's nice to see that though you have solid opinions; your mind is never closed to new ideas, Rachel.

"Let's remember those options for our summary of today's meeting. But let me challenge you a bit on the topic of living arrangements. We've assumed, because we started with retirement facility choices, that the woman making such a move would do so because of age or need of care. What if the new living situation is needed because a woman decides to re-marry? Now where should she live? Her place with him? His place with her? A whole new place?"

Laura chimed in, "A friend of mine, eminently practical, moved into the man's home after they married. He had a house. She had a marketable condo, and it just seemed to make financial sense to sell her place. Well, she made it work, eventually, but I think it was a mistake. She lived with all of the furniture his deceased wife had chosen, maneuvered around in a kitchen where all the utensils and pans had their assigned places — and those were not places she would have chosen for them. It took an emotional toll on her before they sold the house and found their own place. So, I vote: start over with a clean slate. Get a new place."

"All things being equal, I agree with you. All things are seldom equal, though," Susan said, "and I could see one or the other moving into an existing arrangement. Remember what we always come back to: if you communicate with each other about how you feel and how things are working, you can make a go of almost anything."

Ellen added thoughtfully, "Yes, I think the choice of where to live after marriage is definitely an individual one. What might work for me might be horrible for you. A trickier question may be: where are you going to live if you're not marrying him? Putting aside how scandalized the kids might be, and also who has the nicer place, I think the big issue is how to protect yourself in this kind of situation."

"When you're enthralled with someone, it's hard to think about protecting yourself," Rachel said.

"Right," said Kelly. "That's why this is such an important issue for a woman of any age, and especially for an older woman. It seems to me that women must think ahead and imagine some scenarios, and the problems inherent in them. For example, I move in with him; he dies; his children want me out. Now, I'm out. What are my options? Or, he moves in with me; I die; and my kids toss him out. I don't like that, but I'm dead, so I can't do anything. Or we buy a place together, fifty-fifty. Did we do the paperwork right so the house doesn't have to be sold to pay the heirs their fifty percent? Do we both have rights so that the person we've loved has dignity and yet the heirs are taken care of?"

"Yikes, bring in the lawyers," Ellen said, her practical mind at work.

"Yes, awful as that may seem," Eleanor said, "I think one of our meeting summary notes is that: we can't let emotion carry us away. At this time of our lives, with our own finances at stake and the legacies we want to leave our children, we need to consult attorneys and accountants. Our intentions need to be committed to paper, clearly spelled out in 'legalese' who goes, who stays, what is sold, what is preserved, who gets the remains and when."

"Gosh," Kelly said, "I wish it were still as simple as 'Love conquers all.' "

That sparked laughter all around. "I dare you to name a time when love ever conquered all," Laura said. "It's just that at one time we could make ourselves believe that, and now we're too smart."

"Smart . . . hmmm," commented Rachel. "I would say that we can count on experience, rather than native intelligence. Anyone in love with a new man or fearful about a new living experience needs to have some experience to fall back on . . . yes, indeed. And we do have a lot of life experience to draw from!"

"Okay," Eleanor said, "we're about to overstay our welcome here at the library and be forced to look for new quarters ourselves! Let's sum up so Kelly can be sure to have our thoughts on record:

- Life changes, circumstances change. Wise women think about options and possibilities.

- As we age, discussions with family about future living arrangements are especially important, possibly even necessary, for the benefit of all concerned.

- Be sure to think about your own wishes as well as those of the people around you. Remember that you remain in charge of your own life.

- New relationships bring new challenges, including one as basic as where to live. There is no single right answer that fits all personalities. Be sure to seek out the answer that is right for you."

These women are making my head spin! Hard for me to imagine either of my parents with a new partner. Not only hard to think about, but how would I feel? I am glad The Pages believe there is more than one simple answer to this question. At least, I don't have to deal with that today.

And they've got me wondering — would our parents want to live with us? How in the world would we fit them into our house — so different from theirs. We are used to our own clutter and eating patterns. How could I fit someone else into my schedule? And, what if they were sick and needed care? I hope our parents are already talking about this. I'm uncomfortable with surprises!

We Leave Behind a Piece of Ourselves.

Tangible and intangible legacies

There are certain movies and books that we wanted to go on forever. We identified with the characters; we are absorbed in the plot. I've felt this way about my women, especially because they are authentic and original and, therefore, even more compelling than fictional characters.

I was truly stricken, then, when Eleanor announced the last formal meeting of the group. All along, I knew the sessions were limited in number; they had agreed on that at the very beginning. Truthfully, they handled the announcement better than I did. There was still so much I felt I could learn from them, so many issues that I'd liked to have heard them explore further.

The Pages, on the other hand, seemed comfortable with the idea of summing up, talking about final thoughts and moving on with their lives.

~

"The end of our sessions should focus on endings, don't you think?" Eleanor asked.

"Knowing that no one gets out of this world alive, that seems very logical," Rachel quipped. "I think we should talk about legacies, but we should do so from two perspectives. We have things we leave behind, and, being responsible people, we should plan on how to do it. I also want to explore, though, the *intangible* things that we bequeath. What are the intangible legacies we leave in terms of our contributions to our community, as a whole, and to our families, in particular?"

"I love that idea," Ellen said. "I've never been a collector of things, and I once shared with a friend that I felt bad not having glorious old jewelry or porcelain figurines or things like that to leave behind. None of my grandchildren will be able to point to a Hummel or Royal Doulton and say, 'My grandmother bought that a hundred years ago, and now it's invaluable.' My friend, though, said she had accumulated a beautiful set of Waterford crystal glasses, intending to pass them on to heirs, and they were all stolen in a house robbery. It taught her not to put much emphasis on the physical treasures you'll leave behind. So I felt much better in thinking that my legacy would be something other than things."

"I think your comments are very wise," said Eleanor. "Let's be sure to spend a good amount of time discussing intangible legacies. First, though, let's deal with the most obvious of legacies: what we'll include in our Wills."

"We touched on this at some point in our discussions already," Laura said, "but it fits really well here. We said that, as responsible adults and to avoid future family conflicts, we must make provisions while we're alive regarding how property is to be divided."

"Yes, in light of all we've said about the changing dynamics of families, with remarriages and the his-hers-ours arrangements that develop, we want to emphasize the importance of clear and up-to-date Wills," Kelly added.

"My children thought it was a bit morbid and, at first; they didn't want to do it," Ellen said, "but I insisted that they look around the house at the things I've accumulated and decide who would want what when I died. When I saw their startled reactions, I softened it a bit and told them that this exercise would make it easier for me when I decide to downsize, if I ever do. I made a list of their selections and gave a copy to each of them so that there aren't any unrealistic expectations or hard feelings in the future."

"I'm glad that they were a bit reluctant. It would be hard for me to participate in that project, too, and I'm just your friend. You did the right thing, though. I'm adding this to my 'to do list' right now," Laura said, "especially because some of the items in the house belonged to my husband's first wife, and I'm sure there are items that have sentimental value to my step-children that I know nothing about."

"One of the most delightful days I spent with my grandchildren," Rachel said, "was dedicated to looking through my personal items, especially the jewelry and trinkets, so that each one could choose something special they would like to remember me by. Grandchildren seem less hung up on the whole death thing than one's own children do. One of the kids actually said to me one day, 'Mommy said that if our old dog dies, we can get a new one. If you die, do we have to get a new grandmother?' It was said with such innocence that I could only laugh.

"Anyway, we spent a whole rainy day going through my things, and I told them stories about how each piece had fit into my life and why I loved it. They had a good time hearing the stories and asking questions. For me, it was sheer heaven. I got to relive portions of my life with an appreciative audience."

"Great ideas: involve your children; involve your grandchildren; put it in writing. I'm a firm believer in written records," Susan said, "not just because it makes the legal maneuverings after a death so much easier for everyone, but also because I've seen families ripped apart by anger arising from un-met expectations. It seems so much wiser to plan for the inevitable and let everyone know the lay of the land ahead of time."

"Have you seen those kits that guide you through planning your own funeral service? Now that's planning!" Kelly added. "At first I thought, 'Oh, how weird and self-serving,' but now I've come around to appreciate the idea, if not the kit. The less left to chance or misunderstanding, the better."

"I want them to tell jokes at my funeral service. I'd rather leave everyone laughing. At that point, they can't do anything for me. They might as well have a good time," Ellen said.

Laura chuckled as she responded, "You're so organized; you'll probably have a casserole in the freezer so they'll know what to serve for lunch."

~

Laughter, just when I needed it. I realized, intellectually, that some day I'd lose my parents and my older relatives, but I was not ready to accept that, emotionally, just yet. Likewise, I know that my husband or I could die at any time — probably not soon at our ages. We need to talk. We ought to have a Will protecting our children. Maybe I should look at one of those kits, or at least ask my parents whether they have intentions they'd want me to honor. That will be a hard subject to introduce into the conversation. I wouldn't want them to think I'm greedily making plans to benefit myself.

Ah, The Pages were in tune with my thoughts. They were talking about the importance of parents bringing up the subject with children, so that the kids didn't feel like predators.

~

"Just to break the ice a little, I told them I'm worth more to them alive, as a constant source of gifts and assistance, than I will be when I die," Rachel said. "Thankfully, they agreed, but I also told them my lawyer insisted on my having a Will."

"As any good lawyer would," Susan added, "or a financial planner, who has probably seen how assets can dissipate from lack of planning."

"I want to add something here," Ellen insisted. "Considering the advances of medical technology, we need to discuss our feelings about end of life issues with our children, too. It's not just the disposition of Granny and her assets any more. It's about what to do with the shell that Granny may have become."

"Okay," Kelly interjected, "now I'm feeling a little less grown-up and responsible. Yuk! *The shell of Granny?*"

"Well," Ellen continued, "maybe I was a little extreme in my language, but let's face it: modern medicine can keep the body existing long past the point where there is much quality of life or past the point where what I would call 'life' is gone. I have a Living Will, with copies at my lawyer's and with my children, so that there is no confusion about what kinds of medical interventions I want, or don't want, if I'm at the point where I can't speak for myself."

"And how far is that?" asked Laura.

"Not far! This is another instance where I've seen families torn apart by misunderstandings. I don't want my children to fight among themselves about my wishes, and I don't want my assets used up in a futile attempt to defy death."

"I think that's becoming a prevailing opinion as we see those 'shells' you spoke of being maintained on life support for extensive periods of time" Laura said. "But not everyone feels that way."

"Precisely," replied Ellen. "That's the value of a Living Will. You get to say what life support you want while you still have your wits about you and the ability to speak. Decide what you want. That's your prerogative. But write it down in a formal way and let others know. That's my advice."

"So," said Eleanor, "we've concluded that everyone needs a Will for the legal disposition of assets and also a Living Will to provide clear medical directions."

"I've also heard about something called an Ethical Will. I don't remember the exact details, but it intrigued me," Ellen added. "I fear we've run out of sessions for this to be discussed by our group, but I'd be glad to host a gathering to discuss Ethical Wills. As I understand it, an Ethical Will gives you an opportunity to speak to your children after you're gone, when they have time to reflect on who you were and what you tried to teach them."

"Great idea, Ellen," Eleanor said. "Some of us can meet with you, discuss this topic, and add it to our book as an appendix."

"Remember that old high school yearbook thing where the seniors bequeathed some trait to the upcoming classes?" Kelly asked. "I hereby bequeath my giggles during chemistry class . . ."

"And your Elvis jacket?"

"Oh, and my 'pop-it' beads. Remember them? I had them in every color."

"I've heard of friends doing a scrapbook for children and grandchildren along the lines of *Grandmother Remembers*. With the wealth of technology today, it should be easy to make a recording of what grandmother remembers, to go along with a scrapbook, or instead of one," Laura suggested.

"As I was thinking about a legacy, though," Rachel said, "I want my grandchildren to remember what I've stood for. I was a 'feminist' when the word was still new to the language and we had to fight for many of the freedoms young women today take for granted. I contributed to women candidates when they were still a novelty, and when the name Emily was more associated with Emily Post's good manners than with the acronym 'Early Money Is Like Yeast.' I want them to know that I stood for human rights when it was easier to turn away from injustice."

"That was beautifully said, Rachel. I think all of us agree that these kinds of legacies are far more valuable than china or porcelain," Eleanor said. "Let's definitely plan to include the wisdom of leaving Ethical Wills in our suggestions to our readers."

Laura added, "I once worked with a CEO who advised us to write the annual report a year in advance and then spend the next twelve months living up to it. I'd like to suggest that idea to women who are wondering what to do tomorrow or next week. Decide what you would like to leave to your grandchildren as examples of how to live their lives fully. Then go out and create those examples."

"Excellent suggestion, Laura," Eleanor said. "We're not 'good-bye' people, so as we leave today, let's not say good-bye. Let's just look forward to seeing each other in other settings. I'll keep in touch with each of you as I pull together the material you've generated for our book. I feel that you're each a part of my village now, and I'm so grateful for your time and your willingness to talk about these topics honestly and openly."

Susan concluded the meeting by saying, "I love the way Garrison Keillor ends his Writers' Almanac on National Public Radio each morning:

'Be well. Do good work. Keep in touch.' And I'd like for those to be our closing words."

Kelly made her final list of points:

- Make a Will that is clear and fair. Share it with your family to avoid unrealistic expectations that may cause family conflict after your death.

- Make a Living Will so there's no confusion, if/when you're at a point where you can't speak for yourself, about the kinds of medical interventions you want, or don't want.

- To leave a legacy, you must, first of all, create one.

- Live the life for which you'd like to be remembered.

Today's discussion reminded me of my deep disappointment when my Granny died. She had a piece of porcelain that I just loved, and I told her I would like to have it some day. After she died, I learned that it had been given to my cousin. I was devastated! There are things in my family I would like to inherit and pass on to my children — small things that remind me of my childhood home. I guess I'd better talk with Mom about this if I don't want to be disappointed again. And I guess my siblings would like to voice their preferences too.

And speaking of wills: creating a Living Will sounds like a very important task. When Aunt Jane had a damaging stroke and was in the hospital in a vegetative state, I recall the angst and agony of her family about what to do — if and when to remove the ventilator and life support. Then, there is the matter of an Ethical Will. I'd never heard of one before today. What a gift that would be for me and my children. I'm determined to research this and learn more about it

As always, as this last session came to a close, I was left with so much to think about: personal choices about end of life plans, communicating those choices to those I love, an accepting the choices made by my family members.

I'd like to keep these women in my life as my personal guides and mentors. I hope they write that book!

Epilogue

The Eavesdropper reminisces and the real Pages speak up

It's been two years since I listened in on my "Pages." I completed my master's work in literature and now teach at a small college, where I look in wonder at my young students who think they understand the world so well. My own life has taken several twists and turns, including my mother's illness, my aunt and uncle's divorce after fifty years of marriage, and my children's growing autonomy.

The material I gathered from my seven sages has been with me, like wise voices, assisting and guiding me through every one of those turns. I learned so much from them that helped me anticipate important choices in my own life. Their frank discussions and honest searches have provided me with much to ponder, even though we are very different in age. Their lives touched me in so many wonderful and surprising ways. I hope it will be so for you, too.

Kendra T. Brown

Just like the women in the book, I have loved and lost — sometimes tragically. I've been stuck in old roles with ineffective rules and tools. And now I've arrived at a stage of life where some may expect me to rest on my laurels, rest on the porch swing, and, well, just rest.

Rest feels synonymous with rust for me, so that isn't what I do — even when I should. I entered graduate school when my son started his graduate studies, having completed my undergraduate degree in art the same year he graduated from high school. I've been a lifeguard, a secretary, a teacher and a human resources director for a major insurance company. After earning a doctorate, I began practicing as a psychologist in Florida, where I've lived and worked for almost 20 years. I still have a full client schedule.

I count among my treasures my relationship with my son and his family and the love and friendship of my husband. I shamelessly dote on my grandchildren. I am blessed with family: in-laws, step-kids and "ex-laws."

I love to be out-of-doors for almost any reason: playing tennis or golf, gardening, hiking or paddling my kayak. I take piano lessons and, if my schedule ever permits, I'll take lessons in voice, French, Spanish, and painting — but don't tell my husband — that makes him dizzy.

While reflecting on my life's story, I thought that two aspects are noteworthy. First, if you had an aerial view of the journey, you wouldn't see a straight line from origin to some well-defined goal, nor would you see clearly marked signs along the way. A planner would be astonished (and perhaps, dismayed) to see what more closely resembles an array of roundabouts — looping off in first one direction and then another. I arrived at many satisfying places, but they were often surprises. Secondly, you would see how frequently I was aided by others. I simply couldn't have made it without people who stepped forward — often unexpectedly — with amazing generosity.

Thanks to all those "angels" I met on the way who I am recalling now. And, thanks to the remarkable women who unselfishly contributed their stories, their wisdom and their time to become The Pages.

Edith M. Donohue

Baltimore born and raised, I was one of four daughters. I was educated in Catholic schools through college, majoring in biological science. My scientific career started out with a bang! I worked at Johns Hopkins School of Medicine in the department of Physiology, which was headed by the writer of the textbook universally used at the time.

However, shortly after starting work, I married my sweetheart, who was a medical student, and we started our family. That was the end of my scientific career!

After the children were out of the house, I worked in higher education administration in programs for adults returning to school. Since then, my career has been in the field of human resources. I worked in a psychiatric hospital as the training manager and as an associate professor initiating a graduate program in human resources.

Today, I am still working, but I do not have a job. I provide career counseling with a special twist − helping people identify careers and positions that will be fulfilling, that will add passion to their lives − not just matching people to job responsibilities. As a life-long reader and book club member, I facilitate discussion series in two states, Maryland and Florida. In my spare time, I play tennis, kayak, take adult education classes, and I follow theatre and movies avidly. I also regularly enjoy world class music, both orchestral and opera.

Reflecting on my accomplishments, I am most proud of my two amazing daughters, who are successful in their lives and work. Secondly, I'm happy that I was responsible for initiating and managing several new enterprises. I love to get programs off and running.

My early dreams of writing have been realized through several media: business newspapers, professional journals, a workbook for career changers, a book for nurse managers and a how-to book for people who've been down-sized. The books were coauthored with amazingly talented writers and colleagues. As I participated in the development of this book, I marveled at the potential each of us has to live life with passion, enthusiasm, wit and love.

I count myself rich in family, friends and life experiences. I expect the final third of my life to be as full as the first two thirds. Although I am a widow, I have come to realize how valuable all my relationships are and I am not at all lonely. My life is blessed and my hope is to continue to contribute to the world, using my personal resources in service to others as long as I possibly can. After that, I guess I may have time to read all those books that continue to pile up on my tables!

Doris Etelson

Most of my life I've worked to inspire women to reach for the stars. I'm proud of my protégés, who are among those women shattering the glass ceiling in business and industry today. Even after retirement I ran workshops to motivate women. I was thrilled to be awarded an honorary Doctor of Letters by The State University of New York for my contributions to women and to be listed in *Feminists Who Changed America* from 1963 to 1975.

I was born and raised in New Jersey, where I was sketchily trained in my father's restaurant business. I left college at twenty when an opportunity came along to try my own hand at business. For seven years, I ran an industrial catering operation in a large manufacturing plant. I readily admit that my major assets for this enterprise were my ability to write a good proposal for management and the courage to take a risk.

During those years, I married and gave birth to two daughters by "natural childbirth." Our young family moved to an interracial, interfaith community which espoused cooperative land use and tolerance toward others. We hoped it would be a stimulating environment for our children — and it was more than we had even hoped for. I still visit there regularly. I took a four year hiatus from my career, and I treasure the special time we spent there.

In 1960, I re-entered the corporate world, a male-dominated environment that simply wasn't ready for me. Despite resistance at every level, I moved from one "not for women" job to another. I paid my dues in various divisions from food supervision to finance, training to franchise relations, maintenance to marketing, etc. I was eventually promoted to a corporate vice-presidency of that billion-dollar corporation, one of the first women in America to hold such a position. At night, in my "spare" time, I completed my education, earning both a bachelor's degree and an MBA.

Active in the emerging Women's Movement, I became a role model and sought-after speaker, not only for student groups at Harvard, SMU and Simmons, but also for numerous corporate groups. Management wanted to hear about the new role for women from a woman who had successfully combined career, marriage and motherhood.

Following retirement, I served as President of the Woman's Equity Action League in Washington D.C., and later, the Florida Women's Alliance. At the invitation of their governments I traveled to Nationalist China and Russia to meet with women leaders.

Late in 1995 my husband, and greatest supporter for 45 years, died. That caused me to turn inward — to tap a more spiritual and creative vein. I began writing poetry, and I've written a history of the women in our family for my granddaughter. I consciously created memories with my grandchildren, spending years traveling with them one-on-one.

Last, but by no means least, I re-connected with an old friend and business colleague and have once again found deep and profound love. We will soon celebrate our 4th anniversary with joy and gratitude. My daughters, two incredible and successful women, provide me both pleasure and pride. They, too, have produced amazing children. Family occasions with our merged families are warm and lively.

My years meeting with The Pages have been delightful, inspiring, rewarding and irreplaceable. The women have been a gift to my life, and I hope what we have written will be an equally inspiring gift to those who read it.

June G. P. Harry

As a woman born in a mid-sized city on the eastern fringe of the Midwest, and second born, I am probably a typical, straight-forward, compromising-prone, middle-of-the-road, late bloomer.

After completing two years of college, I married my fiancé, who had just graduated. I left college behind. Three children later, my husband opened his architectural practice, and I went to work to help with our finances. Like most women of that time, I chose a field – in my case, real estate – which provided the chance to be at home when my children weren't in school. Fortunately, in later years, I was able to use the knowledge gained there for many successful business and family investments. However, I was ill-suited for sales and soon recognized it.

While considering other career options, I recalled a time – much earlier, when I was only twelve and thirteen – when my father sent me to a local business college for two summer semesters to learn the business basics of accounting, business English, typing, etc. He had expected me to aid him in his office. It seemed to me that I could use these skills and invest my energy in my husband's practice, helping him and our family at the same time. The office staff grew to four when I, too, was included.

I remember being determined to increase profits by at least my presumed salary. I found the accounting tools available from A.I.A. (the American Institute of Architects) insufficient for my purposes. So, I purchased books, information pamphlets and subscriptions that enabled me to develop tools for better office administration procedures and, importantly, for production of the work. Over the years, as the clients and staff grew, it was easy for me to grow with their needs. From "girl Friday", I was promoted to office manager, then corporate vice-president, and finally to chief financial officer, as the clients' projects grew into large corporate, institutional and governmental complexes.

Being "the wife" often meant that others presumed I had simply been given a free place at the table. I felt proud (though quietly) of the many successful audits of our company by county, state and Uncle Sam, in each case receiving compliments on the quality of our records, accounting and production procedures. Once, on an audit of all the major A/E firms in our large county, I was even told that our firm's administration and "books" were the best of the whole lot. I was so pleased — all that research effort had paid off!

Decades later, with continuing research, I was able to accurately appraise the value of our company, and then help negotiate its sale. Sold with an excellent reputation for design, and its enhancing underlying administrative tools intact, the firm is even larger today.

I returned to college and completed my degree at age 70. I'm now happily retired, with time to be with my treasured family, to volunteer and to travel. I feel real pleasure now enjoying those successes that I was able to help our family achieve.

Mary-Jo Hartwell Horton

FIRST is perhaps descriptive of my life experiences and expectations.

First born and only child for 13 years, I was precocious, pampered (but not spoiled), with a persistent desire for perfection – which often frustrated my parents.

First grade was a beginning not to be forgotten. I sat in a chair outside the school room daily as punishment for going from desk to desk chatting with new found friends and answering questions before anyone else had the chance. Mother had taught me well. Miraculously, I learned to sit at my desk and become a serious student, completing high school as the valedictorian (naturally). I went on to obtain a MBA. Later, I was honored by my high school alumni as the *first* woman in the school's annals to become a female executive in a male dominated retail organization.

Ours was a middle class family. My father was a Post Master and served his country heroically during WWII as a colonel in the U.S. Army infantry. My mother was a stay-at-home wife, mother, hostess and patriot. My parent's bachelor friends were my adult playmates who seemed willing to join me at my tea table – sipping water and eating paper scraps. Perhaps that is why I have always enjoyed the association and mentoring of men! My status as an only child came to an end with the birth of my sister, who is now retired as an educator, grandmother and passionate golfer. From both my parents I learned to value working hard and giving back to others less fortunate. I'm grateful for their examples.

For five years, I worked at a local department store (I first worked there as a high school senior over the Christmas holidays). I then embarked on what I think of as an adventure of a lifetime; I went to work for the Department of the Army and spent 2½ years in Heidelberg, Germany – "*Ich Hab My Herz in Heidelberg Verloren!*" It was an experience I will cherish forever. I enjoyed new friends, new cultures, new romances, and I traveled throughout Europe, Africa, the United Kingdom, and Scandinavia.

I returned to the department store, where I was rewarded for my hard work. Ultimately, I became its *first* female vice president and management board member with responsibility for human resources and public affairs, at both the state and local level. I served as Chair of the Governor's South Florida Health Action Coalition. Then, I achieved another first . . . the *first* female board member of a major not-for-profit, 230-bed hospital. During those years, I met and married my husband, who was also a retail executive.

I retired from gainful employment after 35 years, and my husband and I moved to Stuart, Florida, just a few miles up the road from West Palm Beach where I was born, educated and began my working career. During those early retirement years, my husband and I enjoyed being in the mountains of North Carolina and we built a creek-side summer home there. Sadly, he succumbed to Parkinson's disease.

From the beginning of my retirement I found my schedule was busy with unpaid "jobs." I've enjoyed teaching as a professor in two local universities, joined the board of the local health system (subsequently becoming its chair), and I'm happy to serve my former company as a trustee for the retiree medical plan. Other local community organizations and service organizations quickly became part of my life. It seems I'm, once again, hopping from desk to desk, enjoying new and old friends and activities!

Finally, I'm traveling again, visiting Russia, South America, Central America, China, Australia and New Zealand. I've met a compatible gentleman who has become a close, valued friend and companion. Life has been good to me, and I am grateful especially for those who have been with me on the journey.

Dianne Hale Spina

Looking back on my life and putting it down on paper has been a challenge for me. I decided to pretend I was the proverbial fly on the wall, observing my life, and, hopefully, we learned about me together.

South Carolina was my birth place and there it began. I am the youngest of two. When I was 13, we moved to Pennsylvania, where I grew up, married and raised two children (of whom I am very proud). I'm delighted to have two fantastic grandsons.

Life was challenging. I am a shy person and not very outgoing. I was fortunate, however, in my choice for marriage. I married well to a wonderful man who was truly my soul mate. I took on, and fulfilled, roles that were both expected and acceptable: I supported my husband's career, working with him in our business and in our social circles. Meanwhile, I constructed my special support system: my husband, my children and my parents.

That system was shaken to its core when my husband became ill. I focused on being his caregiver. When he died in 2002, I was hurt beyond belief but realized I had to keep going somehow. During and after the mourning period, I continued to live the same life style we had lived as a couple, only now I was without my partner.

One day, I looked around and assessed myself and my life. I found it interesting to see how, all of my life, I had positioned myself as a supporter for others. I felt misplaced and determined to reinvent my life, take off my blinders and look in different directions. I sold the home where my husband and I had lived, made some new wonderful friends and started painting again.

I was thrilled to be included in The Pages. But, at the time, I was still reinventing myself, still trying out my new wings – not completely confidently. These five other women were so accomplished and seemed quite "together" by contrast; I couldn't help but wonder why I was asked to join the group. These women changed my life. Being shy, I didn't speak up much at first. As we kept meeting and talking, I felt so good because this was not about my supporting anyone, but about our lives. My confidence soared, and, one day, something clicked in me.

Today, thanks in large part to these wonderful women, I am growing my social network, painting my fingers off, enjoying my life and looking forward to the days to come.

I love those I supported and am proud I helped them on their way. I am still a supporter of others. But today, I can say with joy: *Now It Is My Turn*.

Pat Austin

Words are one of the loves of my life, after husband, children and grandchildren. Words can be delicious in themselves . . . their sound, their origins, their variations in meaning. More than that, though, I have been privileged in my career in education and public relations to see how significantly words can direct behaviors or change opinions. Used with respect and skill, they can save or mold lives.

So I was delighted at the chance to eavesdrop on the women in this book and capture their words. Some of the women were old friends or acquaintances; others were new to me. All had my admiration long before the end of the project.

It's easy to look at someone's life and say, "Oh how fortunate, everything went so well for them, aren't they lucky?" In fact, people could say that about my life. Having lived that life, however, I know how many times I had to start over, or change course, or promise myself that I'd never do that again.

Here are women who have done well. They have done good. They have also had fits and starts, and they're been honest enough to share with us the triumphs and the pitfalls along with the strategies they developed so that today people can say, "Oh, how fortunate, everything went so well for them."

I savor their words, and I know their readers will do the same.

Appendix A

How to Start Your Own Group

Reading often provides the opportunity for a special kind of dialogue between the reader and the author, or authors, in our case. If our dialogue with you generated some interest, stirred your desire to personally examine important issues we brought up, or if you have other problems and life concerns we didn't consider, you might want to start your own discussion group. We heartily endorse that kind of thinking.

Our group has been invaluable to all of us. Here are some suggestions to get your group started:

- *Someone has to take the lead.* You, perhaps? Or someone you know who is willing to be responsible for scheduling and other logistics. The group leader should be someone who can facilitate the discussions, effectively directing without dictating. Quieter group members will appreciate having a chance to get in their "two cents," and chattier members may sometimes have to be reminded to share.

- *Think of your friends and acquaintances.* You will probably find a mix of personalities and interests. For example, there's someone you would invite to an art gallery, while someone else might be your favorite golf partner. This discussion group will work best for you if you choose women who are likely to enjoy chewing over possibilities, addressing challenges, and who are interested in discussing the various issues that aging presents.

- *When you've selected several women, ask them if they know of others who might be appropriate.* Variety isn't only the "spice of life," it is also essential to the vitality of the group. If everyone is just alike, the options and possibilities will be limited. Members do not have to have the same educational, religious or political backgrounds. Topics might include:

    aging with grace,
    having loving relationships,
    exercising and growing personal power,
    enhancing enjoyment and fun, and
    promoting good health.

  Of course, a willingness to devote a certain amount of time and energy to the meetings is a requirement.

- *Decide how often you want to meet and where.* Sometimes, the meetings can also be social gatherings. On several occasions we met for lunch in a private dining room at a favorite restaurant, other times we "brown bagged" it. We celebrated milestones with wine and cheese. We alternated hostess responsibilities — taking turns at various homes. But, keep the refreshments at a minimum to avoid turning the meetings into a culinary competition. Your local library, church, school or other community centers are also possibilities for meeting places. Make this as easy as possible.

- *Set a time limit for your meetings.* We promise that no matter how much time you allow, there will be times when you won't be ready to stop — but it is important to do so. Observe the structure. We found that 90 minutes was ideal. And, our meetings started on time too. The women you choose will probably have busy lives, so there must be a shared value of time commitment. That can always be renegotiated.

- *Attempt to limit discussion to a single topic each meeting.* If discussion leads in another direction, agree to tackle that another time. These topics can be chosen ahead of time, or may come up because someone has an immediate issue.

- *Decide how you want to record your ideas and conclusions.* We taped our discussions because we wanted to create a book for others to enjoy. You may want to assign someone, and it does not have to be the same person each meeting, to write down the main points and any conclusions reached, and communicate that to the members after each meeting.

- *Review what you have previously discussed before the next meeting. It avoids repetition and frustration.* (Sometimes gals of a certain age do forget!)

- *Agree on a policy of confidentiality.* What is said in the meetings stays there, unless all agree otherwise. It is certainly fine to talk with others about these important discussions, but omit personal references and information. Members must feel comfortable revealing feelings and thoughts to the group. They might not want those shared with just anyone.

- *It is possible that not all your members will be able to attend all meetings.* Every effort should be made to accommodate the various schedules. That is why it is best to pick a special day and time so it can be recorded on calendars. Then, other appointments can be managed around the schedule.

- *It is also possible that someone may have to drop out.* Sometimes life presents challenges that don't accommodate the time spent in the group. Sad as it is to say good-bye to a member, it is not a good idea to bring a new member in after the group has met several times. In an amazingly short time, your group will bond, and then it is difficult to integrate someone new into the mix.

- *How many members make a good group?* We suggest no less than six and not more than eight. Everyone needs to be able to participate.

- *Celebrate the accomplishment of goals.* Celebrate birthdays and other personal events. Celebrate being together. Celebrate the conclusion of your group.

- *Consider some kind of beginning and ending ritual.* An opening thought or even a recitation of the goals for the meeting gets everyone centered. A closing ritual helps to prepare everyone to let go until next time. Closings might simply be the reading of the summary, a round of thanks to everyone for their contributions to the meeting or simply a reminder of the next meeting date and topic. It does not have to be time consuming or elaborate.

In conclusion, we wish you the gifts of new knowledge and deeper friendships that will result from the time you spend together. And you will be part of a growing cohort of women who can be models for daughters, granddaughters, nieces and younger friends. Best of all, you will be living life as fully as possible for as long as you have the gift of life. Enjoy!

Appendix B

Personal Records and Documents

We all have (or should have) important papers, but where are they, and who can find them when they are needed?

Will—

My latest will, dated _____,
is located at/in _____.

The Executor of my will is _____,
whose address is _____
and whose phone number is _____.

The attorney who drew up my will is _____
whose address is _____
and whose phone number is _____.

Other Documents—

Specific locations (e.g., at home in the safe; with the attorney listed above; etc.) should be listed for the following documents:

Document	*location*
Birth certificate	
Marriage license	
Life insurance policies	
Accident and health policies	
Property damage insurance	
Stock certificates, bonds, portfolio statements	
Copy of mortgage or lease	
Bill of sale or title to automobile	
Certificates for burial/cremation	
Tax returns, receipts or cancelled checks	
Military discharge papers	
Divorce/Separation/Annulment papers	
Powers of attorney, including Health Surrogacy	
Documents of trusts	

Document	*location*
Safe Deposit Box # and location	
Social Security No's.	
Other documents:	
Other documents:	
Other documents:	
Other valuables:	
Other valuables:	
Other valuables:	
Other:	

Document	*location*
Other:	
Other:	
Other:	
Other:	
Other:	
Other:	

Permission is granted to photocopy the previous four pages for personal use.

Appendix C

Writing an Ethical Will
(from "Ellen")

Most of us are concerned at some level about how our assets will be distributed when we die.

I imagine most of you have some kind of written will distributing your physical assets: what goes where and to whom. But, what about those values and ideas and experiences you've had over your lifetime? Do you want to share those priceless gifts with your loved ones? And if so, how does that happen?

I discovered, through a friend and colleague, the website www.YourEthicalWill.com, which provides information, access to professional coaching and writing services. You may also find an individual or a local organization offering workshops on preparing ethical wills.

The goal of an ethical will is to answer the question:

What do I want my loved ones to know about me?

I recommend that you begin by making a list of the people you want to have as beneficiaries of this special information. Think about what you intend to convey. You may choose to write one or more letters in place of one document. You decide how you want to create your ethical will.

Next, think about how much of your history or biography to include. Remember how you wished you had asked your parents or grandparents more about their lives? This is a good time to answer those questions for the benefit of your loved ones.

I suggest you write about values. What are your highest values? What are the things you hold most dear? You may need some help identifying your values. If so, you can find lists in career guidance books. Try *What Color is Your Parachute?* by Richard Bolles. Not only does he provide an extensive list, he also includes an exercise to help prioritize your values. You may also want to include how those values have served you throughout your life.

Finally, what other factors have enhanced your satisfaction with life? For example, how did significant relationships contribute? What part did spirituality play? What successes have you enjoyed the most? How did failures influence your life, especially when they provided important lessons? What have you learned?

Although there are workbooks, workshops, coaches and other professionals who can guide you through this process, ultimately, this is your unique creation. Yours will look like no one else's. You may want to include photographs, drawings, letters and even recipes. I hope you will feel free to create something that feels just right for you.

And, finally, if you find the prospect of writing all that to be too overwhelming, use a recorder. You could invite a friend or family member to chat with you about your life, and record this conversation either using video or audio technology — choosing a type with which you are comfortable.

An Ethical Will is a wonderful opportunity to leave a real piece of yourself behind. The thoughts and actions that made you essentially who *you* are can be passed down to your heirs, just like those family heirlooms, or those favorite pieces of jewelry and furniture.

When you've completed your ethical will, you may discover that you, too, have become a beneficiary of it. You will have reintroduced yourself *to yourself.* I believe that an important life task, for all of us, regardless of age, is to reflect on our own personal journeys and their meanings. Such a reflection should be ongoing – a process, not a destination. And the benefits of such an effort will benefit you, as well as those you encounter on your journey.

As you create your Ethical Will, reflecting on your life – successes, challenges and joys – you might want to share those stories with others, in addition to your designated beneficiaries. Oprah Winfrey closes her monthly magazine with an essay titled: "What I Know for Sure." Likely, as with Oprah, there are many things *you* know for sure. I hope you share them.

Oh, and last but not least, this enterprise should be fun. I hope it brings you joy.

Appendix D

Susan's Favorite Gems from The Pages' Talks

Every day is an opportunity to learn
and to make better choices for yourself.

Trust hard-earned instincts.
Then speak up — with good humor, if possible.

We are interdependent. Any relationship
will wither without communication.

Remaining connected is vital. Form as many
networks as you need for social support.

Mutual trust is the first underpinning
of all valued relationships. Kindness is next.

Life means constant change. Stay open to it,
and to its many good possibilities.

We are defined by the choices we make.
May we consider them well.

Suggested Reading
The Pages' Most Helpful Favorites

Books

The Art of Possibility: Transforming Professional and Personal Life by Rosamund and Benjamin Zander

Celebrate Your Self: Enhancing Your Self-Esteem by Dorothy Corkille Briggs (1977)

The Challenge of Age: A Guide to Growing Older in Health and Happiness by E. Fritz Schmerl

The Creative Age: Awakening Human Potential in the Second Half of Life by Gene D. Cohen

Crones Don't Whine: Concentrated Wisdom for Juicy Women by Jean Shinoda Bolen, M.D.

Elizabeth Bishop: The Complete Poems, 1927–1979

Feel the Fear . . . and Do It Anyway by Dr. Susan Jeffers

The Gift of Years: Growing Older Gracefully by Joan Chittister

How to Live: A Search for Wisdom from Old People (While They Are Still on This Earth) by Henry Alford

Inventing the Rest of our Lives: Women in Second Adulthood by Suzanne B. Levine

Looking Good and Feeling Great At Any Age! by Gwen Herb

Love is Letting Go of Fear by Gerald Jampolsky and Jack Kuler

The Mature Mind by H. A. Overstreet

Myers-Briggs Type Indicator (MBTI) instrument by Isabel Briggs Myers

The Next Fifty Years: A Guide for Women at Midlife and Beyond by Pamela D. Blair

On Women Turning 50: Celebrating Mid-Life Discoveries by Cathleen Rountree

Peace is Every Step: The Path of Mindfulness in Everyday Life by Thich Nhat Hanh, Arnold Kotler and H. H. the Dalai Lama

A Place Called Canterbury: Tales of the New Old Age in America by Dudley Clendinen

Successful Aging by Mary O'Brien, M.D.

The Successful Retirement Guide: Hundreds of Suggestions on How to Stay Intellectually, Socially and Physically Engaged for the Best Years of Your Life by R. Kevin Price

A Theory of Personality: The Psychology of Personal Constructs by George A. Kelly

What Color Is Your Parachute: A Practical Manual for Job-Hunters and Career-Changers by Richard N. Bolles

When I Am An Old Woman I Shall Wear Purple by Sandra Haldeman-Martz

About the Author

Kendra T. Brown, Ph.D.

Kendra T. Brown, Ph.D is a Licensed Psychologist with a thriving practice in Stuart, Florida. She received a B.S. in Art Education from the University of Tennessee at Chattanooga, with continued studies post graduation in psychology. She received her doctorate from the University of Memphis (formerly Memphis State University) in the field of Clinical Psychology.

Dr. Brown is a member of both the American and Florida Societies of Clinical Hypnosis, and the Florida Psychological Association. She has written magazine articles, conducted seminars and created instructional videos in the areas of psychology, human resources, sports performance and hypnosis.

She was formerly director of human resources for the field offices of a large national insurance company. She is passionate in her support of educators, having taught students from first grade through graduate school in the areas of reading, remedial English and math, special education, psychology and management.

As a co-founder of Ladies Links Fore Golf, LLC, Dr. Brown enjoyed enhancing the performance of women amateur golfers through workshops, magazine articles and on the LL4G.com website. She continues to be associated with LL4G through guest appearances.

Dr. Brown can be reached through her website:

www.KendraBrownPhD.com